100 ANCIENT CHINESE FABLES

中國古代寓言一百篇

一百叢書

漢英對照 Chinese-English

喬車潔玲選譯 K.L. Kiu

100 ANCIENT CHINESE FABLES

中國
古代寓言一百篇

商務印書館

叢書編輯：羅　斯
執行編輯：曾振邦
設　　計：溫一沙

《一百叢書》
100 ANCIENT CHINESE FABLES
中國古代寓言一百篇
K.L. Kiu
喬車潔玲選譯

出版：商務印書館香港分館
　　　香港鰂魚涌芬尼街2號D僑英大廈五樓
印刷：中華商務聯合印刷(香港)有限公司
　　　香港九龍炮仗街75號
版次：1985年11月第1版
　　　1987年6月第2次印刷
　　　ⓒ 1985　1987　商務印書館香港分館
　　　ISBN　962 07 1057 6

《一百叢書》總序

　　本館出版英漢(或漢英)對照《一百叢書》的目的,是希望憑藉着英、漢兩種語言的對譯,把中國和世界各類著名作品的精華部分介紹給中外讀者。

　　本叢書的涉及面很廣。題材包括了寓言、詩歌、散文、短篇小說、書信、演說、語錄、神話故事、聖經故事、成語故事、名著選段等等。

　　顧名思義,《一百叢書》中的每一種都由一百個單元組成。以一百爲單位,主要是讓編譯者在浩瀚的名著的海洋中作挑選時有一個取捨的最低和最高限額。至於取捨的標準,則是見仁見智,各有心得。

　　由於各種書中被選用的篇章節段,都是以原文或已被認定的範本作藍本,而譯文又經專家學者們精雕細琢,千錘百煉,故本叢書除可作爲各種題材的精選讀本外,也是研習英漢兩種語言對譯的理想參考書,部分更可用作朗誦教材。外國學者如要研習漢語,本叢書亦不失爲理想工具。

商務印書館香港分館
編輯部

前　言

　　根據《辭海》，寓言是"文學作品的一種體裁，是帶有勸喻或諷刺的故事。"（頁2357，上海辭書出版社，1979年版）。這定義指出了寓言的兩個特點：它不但具備勸喻、諷刺的功能，而且是一種有故事情節的文學作品。格言和箴言也有喻世的作用，但沒有故事情節，所以不能算是寓言。

　　談到寓言，一般人很自然會聯想起希臘的《伊索寓言》。我國在這方面雖然沒有那麼聞名，但在幾千年的文學寶庫裏，其實存在着不少精彩的寓言。這些寓言是文學家、史學家、哲學家的心血結晶。他們闡述論點時，為了加強說服力，都喜歡利用一些小故事來作例證，於是陸續形成了許許多多頗堪玩味的寓言。可惜，我國的寓言散見於各類的書籍，要一一找來細意欣賞，實在不容易。幸好最近幾十年有一些寓言選集面世，才填補了這個缺陷。譬如茅盾先生在一九一七年編選的《中國寓言初編》，就曾經滿足了愛好寓言者的需求。近期出版的寓言集不單有詳盡的註釋，還附有白話文的翻譯，更給予讀者不少方便。

　　寓言集的範圍有的很寬，從先秦到清代的寓言都包羅在內；有的較窄，只收集某一個時期的寓言。這個譯集名爲《中國古代寓言一百篇》，所收錄的是先秦至兩漢的寓言，也就是我國最早期的寓言。先秦（特別是戰國）時代在中國寓言發展史上佔有光輝的一頁，這時期的寓言對後代作品有很深遠的影響。要把中國寓言介紹給西方讀者，從先秦時期開始是最適當不過的了。這些寓言最接近伊索的年代，所以對熟識《伊索寓言》而從事中西方寓言比較的人來說，也是饒有意義的。

先秦的寓言是時代的產物。戰國時期，寓言的數量特豐，主要是當時百家爭鳴的局面造成。諸子周遊列國，宣揚自己的學說，爲了得到各國君主的支持，必須想盡辦法去說服他們。寓言就成爲遊說的一種有力武器。用故事的形式來說明自己的論點，總比較直接的陳述有效得多，同時也是一種安全的做法。諸子面對的是喜怒無常的君主，如果隨便進言，很容易招惹禍患，所以需要極高的語言技巧，才能夠達到遊說的目的。因此，運用言簡意賅的寓言，是十分自然的事。

到了秦漢，政治局勢跟先秦時代截然不同。這時期的寓言也就相應地減少了。秦始皇焚書坑儒和漢朝崇尚儒術的政策都側重箝制人民的言論自由。在種種客觀情況限制下，我國寓言缺乏了有利的發展條件。這時期的作品，不過是依據先秦寓言的模式寫定下來罷了。

一般人常有一種錯覺，以爲寓言裏的主角大多數是動物，其實並不盡然。就中國的寓言來說，當然有用動物作主角的，但也有不少和人世間的情事有關；有時更借用歷史人物來增添故事的趣味，使整段叙述看來更具眞實感。此外，我國的寓言也包含神話色彩，《愚公移山》就是一個著名的例子。

　　寓言豐富了我國的語言。寓言簡潔、精練的語言形式成爲了漢語不可分割的一部分。學校的課本也選錄了不少寓言，例如《守株待兔》、《杞人憂天》、《畫蛇添足》等等，都是流播極廣的故事。

　　挑選這本譯集的一百則寓言，其中最重要的一個原則就是繙成英文後，那些只懂得英文的人，也能夠容易接受。如果故事的重點涉及棘手的繙譯問題，那就祇好割愛了。例如，《戰國策》有一個叫《周人賣樸》的寓言，整個故事最精彩的地方，就是"璞"與"樸"這兩個字因爲音近而引起誤會的那一部分。如果把這兩個字音譯，就難免失掉原文的意味。外國讀者面對兩個沒有意義的注音字，也必定會感到莫名其妙。諸如此類的寓言，就不會收錄在譯集裏。

　　除了語言的問題外，文化差異對讀者的理解也構成了障礙——《莊子》裏的《儒以詩禮發塚》，叙述兩個儒生掘墳盜寶的情形。那些對傳統儒家沒有認識的人，就很難體會到故事中深刻的諷刺，所以這個寓言也沒有收在譯集裏。

有些寓言很相似。譯者盡量避免集錄和繙譯帶有相同教訓的故事，例如《戰國策》的《曾參殺人》，指出荒謬的謠言經過幾個人複述後就會變成可信的消息。《韓非子》裏《三人成虎》說的也是同樣的事，所以譯集只選了其中一則。

譯集盡可能選收今天仍為一般人熟識的寓言，特別是那些已經成為漢語成語內涵的故事。除了上文提過的數則外，這些寓言還包括《蟪蚌相爭》、《掩耳盜鐘》、《自相矛盾》等等。

在繙譯的過程中，譯者有一個原則，那就是務求譯文易讀易明，使讀者在領會故事主旨方面不會有什麼困難。

在用註方面，譯者完全不用腳註，以免分散讀者的注意力。如果某字某句的註釋對理解故事真的非常重要，那麼譯者就用短句的形式把註解納入正文裏面。譬如一些和人物或風俗習慣有關的資料是原文沒有的，但對理解故事非常重要，譯者便一一列舉出來——在《韓非子》的《伯樂敎人》裏，譯者交代了以相馬知名的伯樂的長處；在《晏子春秋》的《二桃殺三士》裏，作者用了個"趣"字來表示晏子對三個勇士很有禮貌，但外國人不易明白這個字的含義，所以譯文便直接把這一點加以說明。

如果某些特別名詞需要音譯，在這些注音字首次出現的故事裏必定有註釋。這些註釋對理解重要就放在正文，否則放在篇末。舉例來說，"子"這個後綴放在姓氏之後是男子的美稱，由於讀者即使不知道"子"字的用法也能夠理解故事的內容，正文裏就不加上什麼解釋了。但是，篇末的註釋則交代人物的全名和"子"字的用法，作為提高讀者興趣的附加資料。度量衡方面的名詞需要音譯的也用同一辦法來處理。

繙譯對話時，譯者依據英語的習慣，在適當的地方稍作增減。很多時原文的一句話會分成兩截，說話人的名字則從句首改置在兩截說話的中間。此外，每逢對話必開新段；原文的"曰"字也往往省略，因為上下文和標點符號已經把"曰"字的意思交代清楚了。

中西文化差異也引起不少繙譯問題。譯者解決這些問題時，以遷就讀者為主。舉個例說，我國古代大臣向君主說話時照例自稱"臣"，但把這自稱直譯成英文就會非常突兀。為了使譯文通順而又保留原文中大臣對君主的尊敬語調，譯者刪去大臣的自稱，代之以大臣向君主的尊稱。

這個選集所收的寓言，原都沒有正式的篇

名。原因很簡單：不少故事只不過是作者所舉
的例子，本非獨立成篇。因此同一故事，在不
同的選本裏，會給編者冠以不同的篇名。譯者
盡量選用多數人熟悉的中文篇名，同時也爲每
篇譯文加上英文篇名。選集裏的一百則寓言，
按照年代編排，以便讀者對中國寓言早期的發
展過程有一點認識。

　　這本譯集是譯者近年來的一個小小習作，
不敢奢言對溝通中西文化有什麼貢獻，只不過
想把我國寓言這種文學作品介紹給西方讀者而
已。如果譯文有任何錯漏，敬請不吝指正。

　　　　　　　　　　　　　　　喬車潔玲

PREFACE

A fable is "a short story devised to convey some useful lesson, an *apologue*" (*Shorter Oxford Dictionary*). In A.F. Scott's *Current Literary Terms,* 'fable' is defined as "a short narrative illustrating some moral truth." Thus a distinctive feature of the fable is that it contains "a moral truth." It is unlike proverbs or maxims because the moral truth is presented not in the form of a saying but a narrative.

Whenever one speaks of fables, the ancient Greek fables of Aesop immediately come to mind. Chinese fables as a literary variety enjoy less international attention. Chinese literature is, in fact, rich in narratives that would qualify as fables. These stories were written by philosophers, historians, prose writers, etc., and many of them, especially the early ones, were used to illustrate the writer's arguments. Since Chinese fables are found in different kinds of writings the reader is unlikely to come across a large number of them unless they are collected into a separate volume. This task has been accomplished by diligent scholars, a notable example being Mao Dun who edited a selection of Chinese fables: *Zhongguo yuyan chubian* 中國寓言初編 in 1917. In recent years a number of such selections have become available and, as a result of the labour of the editors, modern Chinese translations are often provided along with useful notes to aid the readers.

Some selections concentrate on a certain period in the development of Chinese fables while others cover almost the entire history of Chinese literature up to the Qing dynasty (1644-1911). The present selection is concerned with ancient Chinese fables and therefore confines itself to the Pre-Qin and Qin-Han periods (roughly from the fourth century BC to the third century AD) which constitute the earliest stages in the history of fables in China. The Pre-Qin period, especially the Era of the Warring States (475-221 BC), was a flowering age for the Chinese fable and exerted a definite influence on works of later centuries. Any attempt to introduce Chinese fables to western readers should start with this period. To those familiar with Aesop's tales, the earliest stories would be of special interest because they are nearest to Aesop's fables in terms of time.

Pre-Qin fables are very much a product of the times. In the Era of the Warring States which produced the richest yield of Chinese fables in the pre-Christian age, different schools of thought vie for precedence in a political scene that was far from stable. Exponents of various schools strove to win the support of kings to carry out their ideas of government or reform. Fables were often used as a tool in presenting their arguments. A short story illustrating a point one wants to make is a far more effective and safer means than putting forth one's opinions in a direct manner. Easily incensed monarchs do not take kindly to criticisms or suggestions that do not correspond with their own views. In this selection the reader will come across fables that have been used to change the minds of rulers who wanted to start wars, execute ministers or embark on various acts of folly.

Due to the change in the political climate the Qin-Han period did not produce many notable fables. Government oppression of scholar-gentlemen in the Qin period and the predominance of Confucian doctrines over all other schools of thought in the Han dynasty discouraged the free expression of ideas and did not felicitate the development of fables. Many Qin-Han fables take pre-Qin stories as their model.

Fables are often associated with stories with animal characters. Chinese fables do include such tales but we also find a large number of narratives with human protagonists. In some instances, fictitious inventions are attributed to historical figures in order to lend credibility to the tale or to increase the story interest. We also find myths among Chinese fables, a famous example being *Yugong yishan* 愚公移山 (*To Move Mountains*), in which the gods took part in the action by giving an old man a helping hand.

Fables have served to enrich the Chinese language. Many popular stories are included in school text books and the morals of these tales have found their way into the language and are still in use up to this day. Some examples are *Shouzhu daitu* 守株待兔 (*The Vigil by the Tree Stump*), *Qiren youtian* 杞人憂天 (*The Worrier of Qi*) and *Huashe tianzu* 畫蛇添足 (*The 'Finishing' Touch*).

The one hundred tales in the present volume are selected according to several principles. One important consideration in choosing Chinese fables for translation is that the end product must be easily comprehensible to readers who only have access to the story through the English translation. If the point of the story hinges on an almost untranslatable literary device such as a pun, the tale would not be a good choice. One example is a fable called *Zhouren maipu* 周人賣樸 found in *Zhanguoce* 戰國策. A pun has a very important place in the story: *pú* 璞 (uncut jade) and *pǔ* 樸 (rat meat that has not been cured). Using romanisation to explain the pun detracts greatly from its effect. Presenting the reader with two meaningless sounds can only alienate him.

Apart from such linguistic considerations, difference in cultural background is another obstacle to the western reader. A story from *Zhuangzi* 莊子 called

Ru yi shili fazhong 儒以詩禮發塚 tells about two *rushen* 儒生 (commonly translated as 'Confucian disciples') digging up a tomb in order to steal the buried valuables. Anyone not familiar with the values and conventions of Confucianism would probably find the story dull and miss the irony that is immediately obvious to the Chinese reader.

When two or more fables serve to bring out a similar moral, only one is chosen. *Zeng Shen sharen* 曾參殺人 (*One time too many*) from *Zhanguoce* 戰國策 shows that even an incredible rumour gains credibility when it is repeated several times. *Sanren cheng hu* 三人成虎 from *Hanfeizi* 韓非子 conveys a similar lesson. Thus only one is included in the selection.

Fables whose morals are still current today and have become part of the Chinese language are chosen as much as possible. Besides those mentioned above, a few other examples are *Yubang xiangzheng* 鷸蚌相爭 (*The Snipe and the Clam*), *Yaner daozhong* 掩耳盜鐘 (*Ostrich Logic*) and *Zixiang maodun* 自相矛盾 (*His Spear against his Shield*).

In rendering fables into English readability is an important principle. Every effort is made to spare the reader from distraction by unnecessary details that would detract from the effect made by the point of the simple story.

I have chosen not to use footnotes so as not to divert the reader's attention from the story itself. Where explanations are absolutely necessary to the understanding of a story they are incorporated into the text of the tale in the form of short phrases. Additional background information concerning certain characters or ancient social conventions is often included in the story. An example of the former is the fame of Bo Le 伯樂 as a judge of horses, while an instance of the latter can be found in *Er tao sha sanshi*

二桃殺三士 (*Two Peaches for Three*). In this story the word *qu* 趨 (quickening one's steps) is used without any explanation that this is a sign of respect. In the translation the word 'politely' is added to enlighten the reader.

When romanisation is necessary for special terms a note of explanation is given at the end of the story at the first occurrence of the term. One example is the *-zi* 子 suffix used to denote a polite form of address. Even without knowing the meaning of this suffix the reader is able to understand the story so no explanation is added in the text itself. The meaning of the suffix and the full name of the person referred to are given at the end of a story as points of interest. The same applies to measurements such as *li* 里, *chi* 尺 and *ren* 仞.

In dealing wtih dialogue, the translation follows the convention of English writings and makes adjustments or allows omissions where necessary. The utterance is often broken up into two parts and the speaker is mentioned after the first part instead of at the very beginning as in the original text. A new paragraph is used for conversation and sometimes *yue* 曰 (say) is omitted when its sense is obvious from the context and the punctuation.

Problems in translation caused by cultural differences are handled also with readability in mind. One example is the Chinese practice of a minister referring to himself as *chen* 臣 when addressing his sovereign. This is a sign of respect but when translated literally the rendition would seem extremely odd to western readers while there is no oddity whatsoever in the original version. In the present translation a polite form of addressing the king is substituted for this mode of self address. "My lord" or "sire" is used to show the minister's respect and at the same time avoid awkwardness in the English version.

The fables in the present selection do not have proper titles. One obvious reason is that many were used as illustrations by the writer and merely form part of a larger text. Thus the same story might acquire various titles from the hands of different editors. The titles used in the Chinese text are usually well known ones and English titles are supplied for every tale by the translator. The one hundred fables in the selection are arranged chronologically in the hope of presenting the earliest stages in the development of Chinese fables.

K.L. Kiu

目 錄

一　五十步笑百步

梁惠王曰：“寡人之於國也，盡心焉耳矣。河內凶，則移其民於河東，移其粟於河內；河東凶亦然。察鄰國之政，無如寡人之用心者。鄰國之民不加少，寡人之民不加多，何也？”

孟子對曰：“王好戰，請以戰喻。填然鼓之，兵刃既接，棄甲曳兵而走。或百步而後止，或五十步而後止。以五十步笑百步，則何如？”

曰：“不可，直不百步耳，是亦走也。”

曰：“王如知此，則無望民之多於鄰國也。”

《孟子·梁惠王上》

1 The Pot Calling the Kettle Black

"I have spent a lot of time and effort," stated King Hui of the state of Liang, "on governing my country. When there is a bad harvest in Henei, north of the Yellow River, I evacuate the people to Hedong, east of the Yellow River and move the grain of Hedong to Henei. When the harvest is bad in Hedong I would do the same for them. As far as I could see, none of the rulers of the neighbouring states are as diligent as I. But the number of people in neighbouring states does not decrease and the number of my subjects does not increase. Why is this so?"

"My lord likes fighting battles," replied Mencius, "so I will use an analogy from war: imagine battledrums thundering and weapons clashing. At this time some soldiers abandon their armour and run away, dragging their weapons behind them. Some stop after going one hundred paces. Others halt after fifty paces. Those who ran only fifty paces laughed at those who ran a hundred. What do you think?"

"That's not right. It's just that they didn't go a hundred paces, but they did run away all the same."

"My lord, if you understand this, then you should not cherish hopes of having more subjects than your neighbours."

Mencius

二 揠苗助長

宋人有閔其苗之不長而揠之者，芒芒然
歸，謂其人曰："今日病矣！予助苗長矣！"
其子趨而往視之，苗則槁矣。

《孟子·公孫丑上》

2 Giving the Seedlings a Hand

A man of the state of Song was worried about his seedlings growing too slowly. He pulled up the seedlings one by one and came home exhausted.

"I am tired out today. I helped the seedlings to grow," he said to his family.

His son hurried to the fields to have a look and found that all the seedlings had shrivelled up.

Mencius

三　月攘鄰雞

今有人日攘其鄰之雞者，或告之曰：“是非君子之道。”曰：“請損之，月攘一雞，以待來年然後已。”

如知其非義，斯速已矣，何待來年？

《孟子·滕文公下》

3   Once a Month

Now there was a man who stole a chicken from his neighbour every day.

"This is not the way a man of moral principles should behave," he was told.

"Well, then I'll reduce the number," he replied, "I'll steal one every month and next year I won't steal any more."

Since he knew he was doing something wrong, he ought to stop at once. Why wait till next year?

Mencius

四 齊人妻妾

齊人有一妻一妾而處室者。其良人出，則必饜酒肉而後反。其妻問所與飲食者，則盡富貴也。其妻告其妾曰：「良人出，則必饜酒肉而後反；問其與飲食者，盡富貴也，而未嘗有顯者來，吾將瞷良人之所之也。」

蚤起，施從良人之所之，徧國中無與立談者。卒之東郭墦間，之祭者乞其餘；不足，又顧而之他。此其為饜足之道也。

其妻歸告其妾，曰：「良人者，所仰望而終身也，今若此！」與其妾訕其良人，而相泣於中庭，而良人未知之也，施施從外來，驕其妻妾。

由君子觀之，則人之所以求富貴利達者，其妻妾不羞也而不相泣者，幾希矣。

《孟子·離婁下》

4   A Shameless Husband

A man of the state of Qi had a wife and a concubine, and the three of them lived together in the same
house. Whenever the husband went out, he would come
back satiated with food and wine. Being asked by his
wife about the people he ate and drank with, he told her
that they were all wealthy men.

His wife said to his concubine, "Whenever our
husband goes out, he would come back satiated with
food and wine. I asked him about the people he ate
and drank with and he said they were all wealthy
men. But no distinguished visitor has ever come to our
house. I am going to follow him secretly and find out
where he goes."

She got up early one morning and followed her
husband stealthily. In the whole capital city no one
stopped to talk to him. Eventually he went to the
cemetery in the eastern suburbs and begged for leftovers
from those who offered food as sacrifices to ancestors
in front of their graves. When he did not have enough he
would look around for other people offering sacrifices.
This was how he became satiated with food and wine.

His wife returned home and told the concubine
everything. "Our husband is the support and stay of
our lives, and now he has degraded himself to this."

The two of them abused him and wept together in
the courtyard. Their husband, knowing nothing of
what had happened, sauntered in and put on airs in
front of his wife and concubine.

In the view of men with a sense of decency and
honour, of all the means people employ to gain wealth
and riches, few would not cause their wives and concubines to weep together in shame.

Mencius

五　醜女效顰

　　　　西施病心而顰其里。其里之醜人見而美
之，歸亦捧心而顰其里。其里之富人見之，緊
閉門而不出；貧人見之，挈妻子而去之走。
　　　　彼知顰美，而不知顰之所以美。

《莊子外篇・天運》

5 Aping a Beauty

Xi Shi, a famous beauty, had a pain in her bosom, so she had a frown on her face when she went out. An ugly girl who lived nearby saw her and thought she looked very beautiful. Therefore when she went home, she also put her hands on her bosom and had a frown on her face.

When a rich man in the neighbourhood saw her, he shut his doors tightly and did not go out. When a poor man saw her, he took his wife and children and gave her a wide berth.

She only knew Xi Shi's frown looked beautiful but she did not know the reason for its beauty.

Zhuangzi

六　埳井之蛙

　　　　子獨不聞夫埳井之蛙乎？謂東海之鱉曰：
"吾樂與！出，跳梁乎井幹之上；入，休乎缺
甃之崖。赴水則接腋持頤，蹶泥則沒足滅跗。
還虷、蟹與科斗，莫吾能若也。且夫擅一壑之
水而跨跱，埳井之樂，此亦至矣！夫子不時來
入觀乎？"

　　　　東海之鱉左足未入而右膝已縶矣。於是逡
巡而卻。告之海，曰："夫千里之遠，不足以
舉其大；千仞之高，不足以極其深。禹之時，
十年九潦，而水弗為加益；湯之時，八年七
旱，而崖不為加損。夫不為頃久推移，不以多
少進退者，此亦東海之大樂也。"

6   The Frog in the Shallow Well

Have you not heard of the frog that lived in a
shallow well? It said to a turtle that lived in the East
Sea, "I am so happy! When I go out, I jump about on
the railing beside the mouth of the well. When I come
home, I rest in the holes on the broken wall of the well.
If I jump into the water, it comes up to my armpits
and holds up my cheeks. If I walk in the mud, it covers
up my feet. I look around at the wriggly worms, crabs
and tadpoles, and none of them can compare with me.
Moreover, I am lord of this trough of water and I stand
up tall in this shallow well. My happiness is full. My
dear sir, why don't you come often and look around
my place?"

Before the turtle from the East Sea could get its
left foot in the well, its right knee got stuck. It hesitat-
ed and retreated. The turtle told the frog about the
East Sea.

"Even a distance of a thousand *li* cannot give you
an idea of the sea's width; even a height of a thousand
ren cannot give you an idea of its depth. In the time
of King Yu of the Xia dynasty, there were floods nine
years out of ten, but the waters in the sea did not
increase. In the time of King Tang of the Shang dynasty
there were droughts seven years out of eight, but the
waters in the sea did not decrease. The sea does not
change along with the passage of time and its level does
'not rise or fall according to the amount of rain that
falls. The greatest happiness is to live in the East Sea."

After listening to these words, the frog of the

於是埳井之蛙聞之，適適然驚，規規然自
失也。

《莊子外篇‧秋水》

shallow well was shocked into realization of his own insignificance and became very ill at ease.

Zhuangzi

li: a Chinese unit of length equal to half a kilometre.
ren: a Chinese unit of length, approximately equal to 2⅓ metres.

七 鵷鶵腐鼠

　　惠子相梁，莊子往見之。或謂惠子曰："莊子來，欲代子相。"於是惠子恐，搜於國中三日三夜。莊子往見之，曰："南方有鳥，其名爲鵷鶵，子知之乎？夫鵷鶵發於南海，而飛於北海，非梧桐不止，非練實不食，非醴泉不飲。於是，鴟得腐鼠，鵷鶵過之，仰而視之，曰：'嚇！'今子欲以子之梁國而嚇我邪？"

《莊子外篇·秋水》

7   The Phoenix and the Owl

Weizi became the prime minister of the state of Liang. Zhuangzi went to visit him.

"Zhuangzi is here because he wants to be prime minister in your place," someone told Weizi.

Weizi was afraid and searched for Zhuangzi in the capital city for three days and three nights.

Zhuangzi went to see him.

"In the south is a bird called phoenix," said Zhuangzi. "Have you heard of it? The phoenix starts off from the South Sea and flies to the North Sea. It does not alight on anything except the noble parasol tree; it does not eat anything except the fruit of bamboos; it does not drink except from sweet springs. At this time an owl got a decaying rat. The phoenix flew past the owl who lifted its head and screeched, 'Shoo!'

"Are you now using your position as prime minister of Liang to 'shoo' me off?"

Zhuangzi

Weizi: i.e. Wei Shi. The -*zi* suffix is attached to the last name of a person to form a polite mode of address.
Zhuangzi: i.e. Zhuang Zhou

八　魯侯養鳥

　　昔者海鳥止於魯郊。魯侯御而觴之於廟，
奏《九韶》以爲樂，具太牢以爲膳。

　　鳥乃眩視憂悲，不敢食一臠，不敢飲一
杯，三日而死。

　　此，以己養養鳥也，非以鳥養養鳥也。

《莊子外篇·至樂》

8 Man's Meat – Bird's Poison

Once upon a time, a *yuanju,* a fabulous bird from the sea, rested in the suburbs of the state of Lu. With great pomp and ceremony the Marquis of Lu escorted the bird to his ancestral temple where a toast was respectfully drunk to it. The ancient music of *jiushao* usually reserved for grand occasions was played. Beef, pork and lamb which were used as sacrificial offerings for important events were spread before the bird.

The bird became dizzy and pined away, not daring to touch a morsel of meat or a cup of wine. After three days it was dead.

The Marquis treated the bird in the way he himself would want to be treated, not in the way the bird would like to be treated.

Zhuangzi

九　養鬥雞

　　紀渻子爲王養鬥雞。十日而問：“雞已乎？”曰：“未也。方虛驕而恃氣。”十日又問。曰：“未也。猶應響景。”十日又問。曰：“未也。猶疾視而盛氣。”十日又問。曰：“幾矣。雞雖有鳴者，已無變矣。望之似木雞矣，其德全矣。異雞無敢應者，反走矣。”

《莊子外篇·達生》

9 The Fighter

Ji Shengzi raised fighter cocks for the king.

After ten days the king asked, "Is the cock ready?"

"Not yet. It is still puffed up with arrogance and puts on airs."

After another ten days the king asked about the cock again.

"Not yet," was the reply. "It still reacts violently to the merest sound or shadow."

Another ten days passed and the king pressed his question a third time.

"Not yet," said Ji. "It still glowers and looks down on everyone."

Ten days passed. The king again asked about the cock.

"It is almost ready," replied Ji. "Even though other cocks make a noise, it shows no reaction. The bird looks like a wooden cock but it is fully equipped to win in a fight. No cock dares to fight with it. They all turn and flee."

Zhuangzi

十 美與醜

陽子之宋，宿於逆旅。逆旅有妾二人，其一人美，其一人惡。惡者貴而美者賤。

陽子問其故。逆旅小子對曰：「其美者自美，吾不知其美也，其惡者自惡，吾不知其惡也。」

陽子曰：「弟子記之。行賢而去自賢之行，安往而不愛哉？」

《莊子外篇·山木》

10 Beauty and Plainness

On his way to the state of Song Yangzi stayed at an inn. The innkeeper had two concubines. One was pretty and attractive while the other was homely and plain. The plain one was made much of by her husband but the pretty one was slighted.

Yangzi asked the innkeeper why he treated his concubines differently.

"The pretty one," said the young husband, "is very conscious of her good looks. That is why I do not find her beautiful. The plain one is very conscious of her homeliness. That is why I do not find her unattractive."

Yangzi said to his disciples, "You must remember this lesson. If you are virtuous in your conduct without being constantly conscious of your own worth, you will find favour with people wherever you go."

Zhuangzi

Yangzi: i.e. Yang Zhu.

十一　匠石運斤

　　莊子送葬，過惠子之墓。顧謂從者曰：

　　郢人堊慢其鼻端，若蠅翼。使匠石斲之。匠石運斤成風，聽而斲之，盡堊而鼻不傷；郢人立不失容。宋元君聞之，召匠石曰：「嘗試爲寡人爲之。」匠石曰：「臣則嘗能斲之。雖然，臣之質死久矣。」

　　自夫子之死也，吾無以爲質矣，吾無與言之矣。

《莊子雜篇・徐無鬼》

11 The Carpenter and His Axe

Zhuangzi passed the grave of Weizi while he was taking part in the funeral procession of a friend.

He turned and said to those following him, "In Ying, the capital city, a man had a bit of chalk as tiny as the wings of a fly smeared on the tip of his nose. He asked a carpenter named Shi to chop it off. Shi brandished his axe, quick as wind, and with great ease chopped off all the chalk without hurting the nose, while the man stood there calmly with no change of expression on his face.

"This came to the ears of King Yuan of the state of Song. He had the carpenter brought to him.

"'Do it again for me,' said the king.

"'It is true that I was able to do it once,' replied the carpenter. 'But not any more. The other partner has been dead for a long time.'

"Ever since the death of my friend Weizi, I too have lost a partner. I have no one to hold discussions with."

Zhuangzi

十二　莊周貸粟

　　莊周家貧，故往貸粟於監河侯。

　　監河侯曰："諾！我將得邑金，將貸子三百金，可乎？"

　　莊周忿然作色曰："周昨來，有中道而呼者。周顧視車轍中，有鮒魚焉。周問之曰：'鮒魚來，子何爲者邪？'對曰：'我，東海之波臣也。君豈有斗升之水而活我哉？'周曰：'諾！我且南遊吳越之王，激西江之水而迎子，可乎？'鮒魚忿然作色曰：'吾失我常與，我無所處，吾得斗升之水然活耳。君乃言此，曾不如早索我於枯魚之肆！'"

《莊子雜篇·外物》

12   A Fish in Straits

Zhuang Zhou's family was poor so he went to the Marquis of Jianhe to ask for a loan of grain.

"Sure," said the marquis. "I will soon get the taxes from my fief. Then I will lend you three hundred pieces of gold. Will that be all right?"

Zhuang Zhou was pale with anger. "On my way here yesterday, I heard cries coming from the middle of the road. I turned round to take a look and found a crucian carp lying in a rut.

"'Crucian carp,' I said, 'what are you doing here?'

"'I am a minister serving the king of the East Sea,' it replied. 'Sir, do you have a little water to save my life?'

"'Sure,' I said. 'I am about to go to the south where I will persuade the kings of the states of Wu and Yue to channel the waters of the Xijiang River here to escort you back to the sea. Will that be all right?'

"The crucian carp was pale with anger. 'I am out of my proper element and have no place of refuge. A little water will save my life, but you have the effrontery to say such things. You would have done better to hurry along to the dried fish shop and look for me there.'"

Zhuangzi

Jianhe: literally means 'overlooking the river.' Some sources say this refers to the Marquis Wen of the state of Wei while others speculate that this person is merely a magistrate.

十三　杞人憂天

杞國有人，憂天地崩墜，身亡所寄，廢寢食者。

又有憂彼之所憂者，因往曉之，曰：“天，積氣耳，亡處亡氣。若屈伸呼吸，終日在天中行止，奈何憂崩墜乎？”

其人曰：“天果積氣，日月星宿不當墜邪？”

曉之者曰：“日月星宿，亦積氣中之有光耀者。只使墜亦不能有所中傷。”

其人曰：“奈地壞何？”

曉者曰：“地，積塊耳。充塞四虛，亡處亡塊。若躇步跐蹈，終日在地上行止，奈何憂其壞？”

其人舍然大喜，曉之者亦舍然大喜。

《列子·天瑞》

13   The Worrier of Qi

A man of the state of Qi was afraid that the sky will fall down and the earth will cave in. The thought that he would not be able to find shelter when that happened worried him so much that he had no appetite for food and slept very badly.

Another man was very concerned about his worried frame of mind so he went to see him with the intention of straightening him out.

"The sky is merely a mass of vapour. No place is without vapour. When you breathe, walk or rest, you are moving about in this vapour all day long. Why are you afraid that the sky will fall down?"

"If the sky is really a mass of vapour. Won't the sun, moon and stars fall down?"

"The sun, moon and stars are also made of vapour. The only difference is that they shine. Even if they fall down, they will not hurt anyone."

"Then what about the earth caving in?"

"The earth is a big mass of soil and rocks. There are rocks and soil everywhere; no place is without them. When you walk or jump, you are moving about on them all day long. Why are you worried that it will cave in?"

The poor worried man, immensely relieved, was delighted and so was the one who enlightened him.

Liezi

十四　國氏善盜

　　齊之國氏大富，宋之向氏大貧。自宋之齊請其術。國氏告之曰：“吾善爲盜。始吾爲盜也，一年而給，二年而足，三年大壤。自此以往，施及州閭。”向氏大喜，喻其爲盜之言，而不喻其爲盜之道。遂踰垣鑿室，手目所及，亡不探也。未及時，以贓獲罪，沒其先居之財。

　　向氏以國氏之謬己也，往而怨之。國氏曰：“若爲盜若何？”向氏言其狀。國氏曰：“嘻！若失爲盜之道至此乎？今將告曰矣。吾聞天有時，地有利。吾盜天地之時利：雲雨之滂潤，山澤之產育，以生吾禾，殖吾稼，築吾垣，建吾舍；陸盜禽獸，水盜魚鼈，亡非盜也。

14 The Art of Stealing

The Guo family in the state of Qi was very rich while the Xiang family in the state of Song was very poor. Mr Xiang went to Qi from Song to learn from Mr Guo how to become wealthy.

"I am very good at stealing," said Mr Guo. "After I became a thief, I managed to support myself after one year. In two years' time I was comfortably off. After three years I owned lots of land and my barns were all full. From then onwards I could afford to give to the needy and I helped many friends and neighbours."

Mr Xiang was delighted. He took in Mr Guo's remark about stealing without understanding how one should go about it. Therefore, he scaled walls and bore holes to get into houses. He took everything his eyes could see or his hands could reach. After a little while, he was convicted of theft and the inheritance left by his ancestors was confiscated.

Mr Xiang was of the opinion that Mr Guo had deceived him so he went to see Mr Guo in order to put the blame on him.

"How did you steal?" asked Mr Guo.

Mr Xiang gave him an account of what he did.

"Oh dear!" said Mr Guo, "You have totally missed the point of what I meant by stealing. I'll explain what I mean. I heard that Nature has seasonal changes and Earth produces fair crops. I steal from Nature's seasons and Earth's produce: clouds and rain give abundant moisture while hills and ponds supply other rich yields. With these I nurture my grain, plant my crops, put up my walls and build my houses. On land I steal birds and animals and at sea I steal fish and turtles. Every-

夫禾稼、土木、禽獸、魚鱉，皆天之所生，豈
吾之所有？然吾盜天而亡殃；夫金玉、珍寶、
穀帛、財貨，人之所聚，豈天之所與？若盜之
而獲罪，孰怨哉？"

《列子‧天瑞》

thing is stolen, for grain, crops, earth, trees, birds, animals, fish and turtles are all products of Nature. Which of these belong to me? But when I steal from Nature, I do not get into trouble. Now precious stones, treasures, provisions, silks, money and goods are things that are amassed by men. They are not the gifts of Nature. If you steal such things and get convicted who can you blame?"

Liezi

十五　海上漚鳥

海上之人有好漚鳥者。每旦之海上，從漚鳥游。漚鳥之至者，百住而不止。其父曰："吾聞漚鳥皆從汝游，汝取來吾玩之。"明日至海上，漚鳥舞而不下也。

《列子・黃帝》

15 Seagulls

A man who lived by the sea loved seagulls. Every morning at daybreak he would go to the seaside and play with the gulls. Hundreds of gulls would come to him and not fly away.

His father said, "I heard that seagulls like to play with you. Catch a few for me so that I can play with them too."

The next morning when he went to the seaside the seagulls swooped about in the skies but none came down to him.

Liezi

十六　朝三暮四

　　宋有狙公者，愛狙，養之成羣，能解狙之意，狙亦得公之心。損其家口，充狙之欲。俄而匱焉，將限其食，恐衆狙之不馴於己也，先誑之曰：「與若芧朝三而暮四，足乎？」衆狙皆起而怒。俄而曰：「與若芧朝四而暮三，足乎？」衆狙皆伏而喜。

《列子·黃帝》

16   Three at Dawn and Four at Dusk

In the state of Song there was a man who kept monkeys. He was very fond of monkeys and kept a large number of them. He could understand the monkeys and they could also understand him. He reduced the amount of food for his own family in order to satisfy the monkeys' demands.

After a while his family did not have enough to eat, so he wanted to limit the food for the monkeys. But he was afraid that the monkeys would not submit to him. Before doing that he first played a trick on them.

"If I give you three chestnuts in the morning and four in the evening, would that be enough?" he asked the monkeys.

All the monkeys rose up in a fury.

After a short time he said, "If I give you four chestnuts in the morning and three in the evening, would that be enough?"

All the monkeys lay on the floor, very happy with this proposal.

Liezi

十七　尹氏治產

周之尹氏，大治產。其下趣役者，侵晨昏而弗息。

有老役夫，筋力竭矣，而使之彌勤。晝則呻呼而即事，夜則昏憊而熟寐。精神荒散，昔昔夢爲國君，居人民之上，總一國之事，遊燕宮觀，恣意所欲，其樂無比。覺則復役。人有慰喻其勤者，役夫曰：「人生百年，晝夜各分。吾晝爲僕虜，苦則苦矣。夜爲人君，其樂無比，何所怨哉？」

尹氏心營世事，慮鍾家業，心形俱疲。夜亦昏憊而寐。昔昔夢爲人僕，趨走作役，無不爲也；數罵杖撻，無不至也。眠中啽囈呻呼，

17   The Master and the Servant

In the Zhou region (around present day Loyang City) lived a Mr Yin who strove to amass riches. The servants who worked for him were often up half the night and had to start slaving for him before daybreak, seldom getting any rest.

An old servant was totally exhausted but the tasks that fell upon him increased even more. During daytime he would do his work with many a groan. At night, tired out, he would fall into a deep slumber. In his sleep his imagination roamed freely and every night he dreamed that he was a king, high above his subjects, handling all the affairs of state, enjoying himself in the royal palaces, getting everything he desired and his cup was full. Upon waking he would revert to his lowly station as a servant.

When someone, noticing how hard he had to work, attempted to comfort him, he said, "Man's life on earth is but a hundred years. Half of that is daytime while the other half is night. During daytime I am a humble servant and my lot is hard indeed, but at night I am a king and my joy is complete. What more can I ask?"

Mr Yin, his heart weighed down by the many things he had to attend to, his whole attention focussed on promoting his family fortunes, was utterly exhausted mentally and physically. At night he fell asleep, also tired out. Every night he dreamed that he was a servant, sent to run errands, sweating and toiling at all kinds of menial tasks. He was scolded, beaten and had to endure all sorts of ill treatment. He would mumble, groan and cry out in his sleep. It was only towards daybreak that he would quiet down.

Mr Yin was very worried about this and went to

徹旦息焉。尹氏病之，以訪其友。友曰：“若位足榮身，資財有餘，勝人遠矣。夜夢爲僕，苦逸之復，數之常也。若欲覺夢兼之，豈可得邪？”尹氏聞其友言，寬其役夫之程，減己思慮之事，疾並少閒。

《列子·周穆王》

seek out his friend for advice.

"You occupy a high and honoured position," pointed out his friend, "and you have riches beyond measure. All this puts you far above your fellowmen. At night you dream of being a servant because sorrow and happiness coming after each other is part of the natural scheme of things. How can you hope to enjoy life both awake and asleep?"

On hearing his friend's words, Mr Yin relaxed his tight control over his servants and lightened his own load of cares and worries. As a result, his condition saw some improvement.

Liezi

十八　燕人還國

　　燕人生於燕，長於楚，及老而還本國。

　　過晉國，同行者誑之，指城曰：“此燕國
之城。”其人愀然變容。指社曰：“此若里之
社。”乃喟然而歎。指舍曰：“此若先人之
廬。”乃涓然而泣。指壟曰：“此若先人之
冢。”其人哭不自禁。同行者啞然大笑曰：
“予昔紿若，此晉國耳。”其人大慙。

　　及至燕，真見燕國之城社，真見先人之廬
冢，悲心更微。

《列子‧周穆王》

18   Return of the Native

A man who was born in the state of Yan grew up in the state of Chu. In his old age he returned to Yan.

On his way he passed the state of Jin. His fellow travellers played a trick on him. They pointed at a city of Jin.

"This is a city of Yan," they said. His face saddened.

They pointed at a tiny temple housing a village god.

"This is the temple of your native village," said they. He heaved a big sigh.

They pointed at a house.

"This is the house of your ancestors," they said. Tears flowed down his cheeks.

They pointed at a mound of earth.

"This is your ancestor's grave," said they. He could not restrain his sobs.

His fellow travellers burst into laughter.

"We were just putting you on. This is still the territory of Jin." He was mortified.

As it turned out, when he reached Yan and really saw the city and village temple as well as his ancester's house and grave, he was even less sentimental than before.

Liezi

十九　愚公移山

太形王屋二山，方七百里，高萬仞。本在冀州之南，河陽之北。

北山愚公者，年且九十，面山而居。懲山北之塞，出入之迂也。聚室而謀曰：“吾與汝畢力平險，指通豫南，達於漢陰，可乎？”雜然相許。其妻獻疑曰：“以君之力，曾不能損魁父之丘，如太形王屋何？且焉置土石？”雜曰：“投諸渤海之尾，隱土之北。”逐率子孫荷擔者三夫，叩石墾壤，箕畚運於渤海之尾。鄰人京城氏之霜妻，有遺男，始齔，跳往助之。寒暑易節，始一反焉。

19 To Move Mountains

Taīxīng and Wangwu are two mountains with an area of seven hundred *li* square and rise to a great height of thousands of *ren*. They were originally situated south of Jizhou and north of Heyang.

North of the mountains lived an old man called Yugong (literally 'foolish old man') who was nearly ninety years old. Since his home faced the two mountains, he was troubled by the fact that they blocked the way of the inhabitants who had to take a roundabout route whenever they went out. He gathered his family together to discuss the matter.

"Let us do everything in our power to flatten these forbidding mountains so that there is a direct route to the south of Yuzhou reaching the southern bank of the Han River. What do you say?"

Everyone applauded his suggestion. His wife voiced her doubts.

"You are not strong enough even to remove a small hillock like Kuifu. How can you tackle Taīxīng and Wangwu? And where would you dump the earth and rocks?"

"We can dump it into the edge of the Bo Sea and north of Yintu," said everyone.

Therefore Yugong took with him three sons and grandsons who could carry a load on their shoulders. They broke up rocks and dug up mounds of earth which were transported to the edge of the Bo Sea in baskets. His neighbour, a widow by the name of Jingcheng, had a posthumous son who was just at the age of discarding his silk teeth. This vivacious boy jumped at the chance of giving them a hand. From winter through summer the workers only returned home once.

河曲智叟笑而止之曰：“甚矣，汝之不惠！以殘年餘力，曾不能毀山之一毛，其如土石何？”北山愚公長息曰：“汝心之固，固不可徹，曾不若霜妻弱子！雖我之死，有子存焉，子又生孫，孫又生子，子又有子，子又有孫，子子孫孫，無窮匱也，而山不加增，何苦而不平？”河曲智叟亡以應。

　　操蛇之神聞之，懼其不已也，告之於帝。帝感其誠，命夸蛾氏二子負二山，一厝朔東，一厝雍南，自此冀之南，漢之陰，無壟斷焉。

《列子‧湯問》

An old man called Zhisou (literally 'wise old man') who lived in Hequ, near a bend of the Yellow River, was amused and dissuaded Yugong.

"How can you be so foolish? With your advanced years and the little strength that you have left, you cannot even destroy a blade of grass on the mountain, not to speak of its earth and stone."

Yugong from north of the mountains heaved a long sigh. "You are so obstinate that you do not use your reason. Even the widow and her little son do better than you. Though I die, my son lives on. My son produces a grandson and in turn the grandson has a son of his own. Sons follow sons and grandsons follow sons. My sons and grandsons go on and on without end but the mountains will not grow in size. Then why worry about not being able to flatten them?"

Zhisou of Hequ was bereft of speech.

The god of the mountains who held a snake in his hand heard about this and was afraid that Yugong would not stop digging at the mountains. He reported the matter to the king of the gods who was moved by Yugong's sincerity. The king commanded the two sons of Kua'eshi, a god with great strength, to carry away the two mountains on their backs: one was put east of Shuozhou and the other south of Yongzhou. From that time onwards no mountain stood between the south of Jizhou and the southern bank of the Han River.

Liezi

二十 夸父追日

　　夸父不量力，欲追日影，逐之於隅谷之
際。渴欲得飲，赴飲河、渭；河、渭不足，將
走北飲大澤。未至，道渴而死。

《列子·湯問》

20 In Pursuit of the Sun

A legendary giant Kua Fu, overrating his own abilities, wanted to catch up with the sun. He followed the sun to its setting place at a valley far away and became very thirsty. Badly needing a drink of water, he went to the Yellow River and the River Wei to quench his thirst, but the waters from these two rivers were not sufficient to satisfy him. He decided to go to the great lake in the north to drink its waters. Before he got there he died of thirst on the way.

Liezi

二十一 兩小兒辯日

孔子東游，見兩小兒辯鬭。問其故。

一兒曰：“我以日始出時去人近，而日中時遠也。”一兒以日初出遠，而日中時近也。

一兒曰：“日初出大如車蓋，及日中則如盤盂。此不爲遠者小而近者大乎？”

一兒曰：“日初出滄滄涼涼，及其日中，如探湯。此不爲近者熱而遠者涼乎？”

孔子不能決也。兩小兒笑曰：“孰爲汝多知乎？”

《列子·湯問》

21   An Argument about the Sun

When Confucius was travelling in the eastern part of the country, he came upon two children hot in argument, so he asked them to tell him what it was all about.

"I think," said one child, "that the sun is near to us at daybreak and far away from us at noon."

The other contended that the sun was far away at dawn and nearby at midday.

"When the sun first appears," said one child, "it is as big as the canopy of a carriage, but at noon it is only the size of a plate or a bowl. Well, isn't it true that objects far away seem smaller while those nearby seem bigger?"

"When the sun comes out," pointed out the other, "it is very cool, but at midday it is as hot as putting your hand in boiling water. Well, isn't it true that what is nearer to us is hotter and what is farther off is cooler?"

Confucius was unable to settle the matter for them.

The two children laughed at him, "Who says you are a learned man?"

Liezi

二十二　詹何釣魚

　　詹何以獨繭絲爲綸，芒鍼爲鈎，荆篠爲竿，剖粒爲餌，引盈車之魚，於百仞之淵。汩流之中，綸不絕，鈎不伸，竿不橈。

　　楚王聞而異之，召問其故。詹何曰：“臣聞先大夫之言，蒲且子之弋也，弱弓纖繳，乘風振之，連雙鶬於青雲之際，用心專，動手均也。臣因其事，放而學釣，五年始盡其道。當臣之臨河持竿，心無雜慮，唯魚之念。投綸沉鈎，手無輕重，物莫能亂。魚見臣之鈎餌，猶沉埃聚沫，吞之不疑，所以能以弱制彊，以輕致重也。”

《列子·湯問》

22 Zhan Hé the Angler

Zhan Hé used a single strand of silken thread for a line, a sharp pointed needle for a hook, a slender bamboo grown in the Chu region for a rod and split grains of rice for bait. He managed to catch a cartload of fish from bottomless abysses and rushing rapids, without breaking his line, stretching his hook or bending his rod.

The king of the state of Chu heard about this and thought it was extraordinary. He sent for Zhan Hé to ask him how he did it.

"Sire," said Zhan Hé, "I heard my late father say that when the skilled archer Pu Qiezi shot at birds, he had a rather flimsy bow and used a slender string to attach to his retrievable arrow which was shot along the direction of the wind. He hit two orioles in the clouds with one arrow because of his total concentration and the exquisite evenness of his touch. Sire, I used him as an example and learned to fish. It took me five years to perfect my technique. When I come to the river bank with a rod in my hand, I have no other thoughts in my mind except fishing. When I cast the line and let the hook sink into the water, my touch is neither too heavy nor too light and nothing can distract me. To the fishes, my hook and bait seem like bits of mud and froth in the water, so they swallow them without suspecting anything. This is how strength can be overcome by weakness and what is heavy can be got by what is light."

Liezi

二十三　薛譚學謳

　　薛譚學謳於秦青，未窮青之技，自謂盡之，遂辭歸。

　　秦青弗止，餞於郊衢，撫節悲歌，聲振林木，響遏行雲。薛譚乃謝求反，終身不敢言歸。

《列子·湯問》

23 A Subtle Hint

Xue Tan took singing lessons from Qin Qing, a famous singer in the state of Qin. Before learning all that Qin had to teach him Xue claimed that he had mastered all of Qin's skills and asked to leave.

Qin did not try to stop him but gave a farewell dinner for him by a main road in the suburbs. There Qin sang a moving song, beating time all the while. The song seemed to shake the trees of the forest and check the drifting clouds in their tracks.

Xue immediately apologised to his teacher and asked that he be taken back as a pupil. After this, Xue dared not mention going home again throughout his life.

Liezi

二十四　野人獻曝

　　昔者宋國有田夫，常衣緼黂，僅以過冬。暨春東作，自曝於日，不知天下之有廣廈、隩室，緜纊、狐狢。顧謂其妻曰：「負日之暄，人莫知者，以獻吾君，將有重賞。」

《列子·楊朱》

24   Make a Present of Sunshine

In olden times there was a peasant in the state of
Song who wore clothes woven with tangled hemp and
barely made it through the cold winter. When spring
came he enjoyed the warmth of the sun while working
in the fields. He did not know that in this world there
are tall buildings and cosy, warm houses, and he knew
nothing about clothes with silk wadding or furs made
from the skins of foxes and racoon dogs.

The peasant turned to his wife and said, "It is so
warm under the sun. I don't think other people know
about this. If we present this to our king we are sure to
get a rich reward."

Liezi

二十五　道見桑婦

晉文公出，會欲伐衞。公子鋤仰天而笑。公問："何笑？"曰："臣笑鄰之人有送其妻適私家者，道見桑婦，悅而與言。然顧視其妻，亦有招之者矣。臣竊笑此也。"

公寤其言，乃止，引師而還。未至，而有伐其北鄙者矣。

《列子·說符》

25 Served with the Same Sauce

Duke Wen of the state of Jin led his army out of Jin with the intention of attacking the state of Wei. On seeing this, his son Prince Chu threw back his head and laughed.

"Why are you laughing?" asked the duke.

"I am laughing at my neighbour," replied his son. "He was escorting his wife to her father's house. On the way, he saw a woman picking mulberry leaves and he boldly struck up a friendly conversation with her. But when he turned to look for his wife, he saw that someone was trying to flirt with her too. I just find this incident very diverting."

The duke understood his son's meaning. He gave up the idea of attacking Wei and brought his troops home. Before he got there the northern border of his state came under attack.

Liezi

二十六　牝牡驪黃

　　秦穆公謂伯樂曰：“子之年長矣，子姓有可使求馬者乎？”伯樂對曰：“良馬，可形容筋骨相也；天下之馬者，若滅若沒，若亡若失，若此者絕塵弭轍。臣之子皆天才也，可告以良馬，不可告以天下之馬也。臣有所與共擔纏薪菜者，有九方皋。此其於馬，非臣之下也。請見之。”穆公見之，使行求馬。

　　三月而反，報曰：“已得之矣，在沙丘。”穆公曰：“何馬也？”對曰：“牝而黃。”使人往取之，牡而驪。穆公不說，召伯樂而謂之曰：“敗矣，子所使求馬者，色物牝牡尙弗能知，又何馬之能知也？”伯樂喟然太息曰：“一至於此乎？是乃其所以千萬臣而無數者也。若皋

26   True Discernment

Duke Mu of the state of Qin said to Bo Le who was famous for his ability to judge horses, "Sir, you are advanced in years.   Is there anyone in your family I could send to look for fine steed?"

"Good horses can be judged by observing their appearance, by looking at the bones and muscles," replied Bo Le.   "But for a rare horse that has no equal, its characteristics are elusive, almost impossible to pin down.   It is so swift and its tread so light that when it gallops, its hoofs do not stir the dust and no prints are left behind.   My sons have little ability.   They could tell you what good horses are like, but they could say nothing about an incomparable steed.   I have a friend who used to chop and carry firewood with me, Jiufang Gao.   He is, to say the least, as good a judge of horses as I am.   Please send for him."

The duke summoned Jiufang Gao and commissioned him to find an unequalled horse.   After three months he reported back to the duke.

"I have found it, in a place called Shaqiu."

"What sort of a horse is it?" asked the duke.

"It is a bay mare," replied Jiufang Gao.

The duke sent some men to bring the horse back.   It turned out to be a male horse black in colour.   The duke was displeased.   He summoned Bo Le.

"It is too bad," said the duke, "the man you recommended to send on a search for fine horses cannot even distinguish between horses and mares or the different colours of their coats.   What can he know about horses?"

Bo Le heaved a sigh.   "Has it come to this?   This is exactly where his expertise is a thousand times better

之所觀，天機也。得其精而忘其麤；在其內而
忘其外。見其所見，不見其所不見，視其所視
而遺其所不視。若皋之相馬，乃有貴乎馬者
也！"馬至，果天下之馬也。

《列子·說符》

than mine and is too deep to fathom. What he sees is the mystery of Nature. He captures the essence and forgets the dross. He gets the content and forgets the form. He only sees what he is looking for and does not see what he considers unimportant. He only observes what is worthy of observation and leaves out what he deems not deserving attention. In fact, Jiufang Gao's ability is much more valuable than the mere competence to judge the merit of a horse."

When the horse arrived, it really turned out to be an incomparable steed.

Liezi

二十七　楊布打狗

　　楊朱之弟曰布，衣素衣而出；天雨，解素
衣，衣緇衣而反。其狗不知，迎而吠之。楊布
怒，將撲之。楊朱曰：「子無撲矣！子亦猶是
也。響者使汝狗白而往，黑而來，豈能無怪
哉？」

《列子・說符》

27 A Change of Colour

Yang Zhu, the famous philosopher, had a younger brother named Yang Bu who, once, went out dressed in white. It began to rain so Yang Bu took off his white clothes and returned home dressed in black. His dog, failing to recognize him, rushed forward to bark at him. Yang Bu was angry and wanted to beat the animal.

"Don't beat the dog," said Yang Zhu, "you would have acted in the same way. If your dog had gone out a white dog and then came home black all over, wouldn't you have thought it very strange?"

Liezi

二十八　不死之道

　　昔人言有知不死之道者。燕君使人受之，不捷，而言者死。燕君甚怒其使者，將加誅焉。幸臣諫曰：“人所憂者莫急乎死；己所重者莫過乎生。彼自喪其生，安能令君不死也？”乃不誅。

《列子‧說符》

28 Physician, Heal Thyself

Once upon a time, a man claimed that he knew the secret of everlasting life. The king of the state of Yan sent a messenger to learn this secret from him. Before the messenger succeeded, the man who made the claim died.

The king was very vexed with his messenger and intended to put him to death.

One of the king's ministers who enjoyed his trust dissuaded him. "Of man's worries nothing is more pressing than death. Of all the things that are valued by man, nothing is more precious than life. This man lost his own life. Then how could he have taught you not to lose yours?"

The king did not put the messenger to death.

Liezi

二十九　亡鈇疑鄰

人有亡鈇者，意其鄰之子。視其行步，竊鈇也；顏色，竊鈇也；言語，竊鈇也；作動、態度，無爲而不竊鈇也。

俄而抇其谷而得其鈇。他日復見其鄰人之子，動作、態度，無似竊鈇者。

《列子・說符》

29   In the Eyes of the Beholder

A man who lost his axe suspected his neighbour's son of stealing it. To him, as he observed the boy, the way the lad walked, the expression on his face, the manner of his speech — in fact everything about his appearance and behaviour betrayed that he had stolen the axe.

Not long afterwards the man found his axe while digging in his cellar. When he saw his neighbour's son again, nothing about the boy's behaviour nor appearance seemed to suggest that he had stolen the axe.

Liezi

三十　康衢長者

　　　康衢長者，字僮曰"善搏"，字犬曰"善
噬"。賓客不過其門者三年。長者怪而問之，
乃實對。於是改之，賓客往復。

《尹文子‧大道下》

30　Name Versus Fact

An old man who lived beside a thoroughfare named his servant boy 'fighter' and his dog 'biter'. For three years no one came to his house to visit him.

The old man was puzzled. He made enquiries and was told the truth. Therefore he changed the names of his servant boy and his dog, and he had a stream of visitors.

Yinwenzi

三十一 宥坐之器

　　　　孔子觀於魯桓公之廟，有欹器焉。孔子問
於守廟者曰：“此爲何器？”守廟者曰：“此蓋
爲宥坐之器。”孔子曰：“吾聞宥坐之器者，虛
則欹，中則正，滿則覆。”孔子顧謂弟子曰：
“注水焉！”弟子挹水而注之，中而正，滿而
覆，虛而欹。

　　　　孔子喟然而歎曰：“吁！惡有滿而不覆者
哉！”

《荀子·宥生》

31 An Admonitory Vessel

On a visit to the temple of Duke Huan of the state of Lu Confucius came upon a 'leaning vessel'. He asked the keeper of the temple about it.

"What vessel is this?"

"This vessel," replied the keeper, "is put on the right hand side of one's seat to serve an admonitory purpose."

"I have heard," said Confucius, "that such an admonitory vessel would lean to one side when it is empty, stand upright when its contents are just the right amount, and fall down when it is full."

He turned to his disciples. "Pour water into it."

His disciples ladled water into the vessel. When the amount was neither too little nor too much the vessel stood upright; when the vessel was full it fell down; when it was empty it leaned to one side.

Confucius heaved a sigh. "Alas! A fall is inevitable for one who is full of his own worth."

Xunzi

三十二　信子而疑鄰

　　宋有富人，天雨牆壞。其子曰：“不築，必將有盜。”其鄰人之父亦云。暮而果大亡其財。其家甚智其子，而疑鄰人之父。

《韓非子·說難》

32　The Son and the Neighbour

In the state of Song lived a rich man. A heavy downpour caused the wall of his house to crumble.

"If the wall is not mended," pointed out his son, "we'll have thieves coming in." The old man next door said the same thing.

At night, his house was really burgled and he lost many of his valuables. The whole family of the rich man praised the cleverness of their boy but was suspicious about the old man next door.

Hanfeizi

三十三 和氏璧

　　楚人和氏得玉璞楚山中，奉而獻之厲王。厲王使玉人相之，玉人曰："石也。"王以和為誑，則刖其左足。

　　及厲王薨，武王即位。和又奉其璞而獻之武王。武王使玉人相之。又曰："石也。"王又以和為誑，而刖其右足。

　　武王薨，文王即位。和乃抱其璞而哭於楚山之下，三日三夜，泣盡而繼之以血。

　　王聞之，使人問其故，曰："天下之刖者多矣，子奚哭之悲也？"和曰："吾非悲刖也。悲夫寶玉而題之以石，貞士而名之以誑。此吾所以悲也。"

　　王乃使玉人理其璞而得寶焉，遂命曰"和氏之璧"。

《韓非子‧和氏》

33 The Jade of Hé

A man of the state of Chu named Bian Hé found a piece of uncut jade in the Chu mountain. Holding the jade with both hands he respectfully presented it to King Li. The king ordered a jade craftsman to examine it.

"This is stone," said the craftsman.

The king thought that Bian Hé was trying to deceive him so he gave orders to cut off his left foot.

After the death of King Li, King Wu ascended the throne. Again Bian Hé came with the jade in his hands to present it to King Wu. King Wu ordered a jade craftsman to examine it.

"This is stone," said the craftsman again.

The king also thought Bian Hé was trying to deceive him, so he gave orders to cut off his right foot.

After the death of King Wu, King Wen came to the throne. Bian Hé took the piece of uncut jade in his arms and wept at the foot of the Chu mountain. He wept for three days and three nights. When he had no more tears he wept blood.

This came to the ears of the king and he sent someone to ask Bian Hé the reason for his grief.

"There are many men who had their feet cut off as punishment," said the king's messenger, "why do you weep so bitterly?"

"I am not sad because my feet were cut off," replied Bian Hé. "I grieve because a precious stone is considered a common rock and an upright and loyal man is branded a liar. This is the cause of my sorrow."

The king ordered jade craftsmen to cut open the stone. They discovered a piece of precious jade which was thereupon named the Jade of Hé.   *Hanfeizi*

三十四　紂爲象箸

昔者紂爲象箸而箕子怖。以爲："象箸必不加於土鉶，必將犀玉之杯。象箸玉杯，必不羹菽藿，則必旄象豹胎。旄象豹胎，必不衣短褐而食於茅屋之下，則錦衣九重，廣室高臺。吾畏其卒，故怖其始。"

居五年，紂爲肉圃，設炮烙，登糟邱，臨酒池。紂遂以亡。

《韓非子·喻老》

34   Ivory Chopsticks for a Start

In the ancient times Emperor Zhou of the Shang dynasty used chopsticks made of ivory. On observing this, Jizi, a respected minister, was filled with anxiety.

He reasoned thus: "Ivory chopsticks would not be used with earthenware dishes. There would surely be wine cups made from rhinoceros' horns and jade. Ivory chopsticks and jade cups would not go with simple fare. There would surely be delicacies such as the embryos of the yak, elephant and panther. One who tastes such delicacies would not wear clothes made of rough material or dwell in a thatched cottage. He would be clothed in layers of beautiful brocade and live in a mansion, big and imposing. I am afraid for his end. That is why the beginnings of luxurious living fill me with anxiety."

After five years, the emperor built a garden where he hung slabs of meat, and set up copper grills. Grains from distilleries piled up like hillocks and there was enough wine to fill pools. As a result of such extravagances, Emperor Zhou was overthrown.

Hanfeizi

Jizi: i.e. Ji Xuyu, the uncle of Emperor Zhou

三十五　宋人刻楮

　　宋人有爲其君以象爲楮葉者，三年而成。豐殺莖柯，毫芒繁澤，亂之楮葉之中而不可別也。此人遂以功食祿於宋邦。

　　列子聞之曰：「使天地三年而成一葉，則物之有葉者寡矣。」

《韓非子・喩老》

35   A Leaf in Three Years

In the state of Song a man carved a mulberry leaf out of ivory for his king. It took him three years to finish the job. With its pleasing shape, delicate veins, fine hairs and lustrous colour, the ivory leaf, when put among real mulberry ones, was not distinguishable from the rest. Therefore, this man received a salary from the Song government because of his merit.

Liezi heard of this. "If it takes three years for Mother Nature to produce a leaf," he pointed out, "then anything that has leaves would become a rarity."

Hanfeizi

Liezi: i.e. Lie Yukou

三十六　趙襄主學御

　　趙襄主學御於王子期，俄而與子期逐，三
易馬而三後。襄主曰：“子之敎我御，術未盡
也。”對曰：“術已盡，用之則過也。凡御之
所貴，馬體安於車，人心調於馬，而後可以進
速致遠。今君後則欲逮臣，先則恐逮於臣。夫
誘道爭遠，非先則後也。而先後心在於臣，上
何以調於馬？此君之所以後也。”

《韓非子·喩老》

36   A Matter of the Mind

King Xiang of the state of Zhao learned the skill of driving a carriage from Wang Ziqi. After sometime the king raced with Wang. He changed horses three times but every time he trailed behind Wang.

"In teaching me to drive a carriage you have held something back," said the king.

"I have taught you all I know," Wang replied. "But you have not used my skill in the proper way. The important thing about driving a carriage is that the horses' bodies should feel comfortable with the carriage and the driver's mind should be in harmony with the horses. Then you can achieve great speed and go long distances. Now when you are behind me, sire, you want to catch up with me, and when you are in front of me you are afraid I would catch up with you. When driving carriages in long distance races one is either in front or behind. And no matter whether you are leading or trailing your mind is set on me. Then how can it be in harmony with the horses? This is why you could not catch up with me."

Hanfeizi

三十七　遠水不救近火

　　　　魯穆公使衆公子，或宦於晉，或宦於荆。
犁鉏曰：“假人於越而救溺子，越人雖善游，
子必不生矣。失火而取水於海，海水雖多，火
必不滅矣。遠水不救近火也。今晉與荆雖强，
而齊近魯，患其不救乎？”

《韓非子·說林上》

37   Ineffectual Aid

Duke Mu of the state of Lu sent his sons to the states of Jin and Chu to occupy high positions in their governments.

His minister Li Chu said, "If your son is drowning and you send for a man from the state of Yue so far away to come and save the child, then your son cannot be saved even though the men of Yue are good swimmers. If a fire breaks out and you fetch water from the sea to put it out, then even though the water from the sea is abundant, the fire will not be put out. Water far away is useless to the fire at hand. The states of Jin and Chu are indeed strong and powerful, but the state of Qi is near to Lu. If we are imperilled, how can Jin and Chu come to our aid in time?"

Hanfeizi

三十八　魯人之越

魯人身善織屨，妻善織縞，而欲徙於越。或謂之曰：“子必窮矣。”魯人曰：“何也？”曰：“屨為履之也，而越人跣行。縞為冠之也，而越人被髮。以子之所長，游於不用之國，欲使無窮，其可得乎？”

《韓非子·說林上》

38   Hardly a Wise Move

A man of the state of Lu was skilled in weaving hemp sandals while his wife was good at weaving fine white silk. The couple thought of moving to the state of Yue in the south.

"You will be in dire straits," he was told.

"Why?" asked the man of Lu.

"Hemp sandals are for walking but the people of Yue walk barefoot. White silk is for making hats but the people of Yue go about bare-headed. If you go to a place where your skills are utterly useless, how can you hope to do well?"

Hanfeizi

三十九　伯樂教人

　　　　伯樂教其所憎者相千里之馬，教其所愛者
相駑馬。以千里之馬時一有，其利緩；駑馬日
售，其利急。

《韓非子・說林下》

39   A Matter of Discrimination

Bo Le, famous for his ability to judge horses, taught those whom he disliked how to spot fine horses that could cover a thousand *li* in one day. As to people he liked, he taught them to be a good judge of ordinary horses, not particularly fleet of foot. It is very seldom that one discovers a fine steed and such profits are slow in coming. Ordinary horses are sold every day and one could make money in a very short time.

Hanfeizi

四十　就蟲自殺

蟲有蚘者，一身兩口，爭食相齕，遂相殺
也。

《韓非子・說林下》

40   A Snake with Two Mouths

A certain venomous snake had two mouths which bit at each other, fighting over food.   The struggle ended in death for both.

Hanfeizi

四十一　不待滿貫而去

　　　　有與悍者鄰，欲賣宅而避之。人曰："是
其貫將滿矣，子姑待之。"答曰："吾恐其以
我滿貫也。"遂去之。

《韓非子·說林下》

41 Unwise to Wait

A man had a neighbour who was a malicious brute. He wanted to sell his house and get away from the fellow.

"His sins will soon come to a head and he will have his just deserts," he was told, "why not wait a little while?"

"I am afraid," he replied, "that his sins will come to a head through me." So he moved.

Hanfeizi

四十二　中行文子出亡

晉中行文子出亡，過於縣邑。從者曰："此
嗇夫，公之故人，公奚不休舍？且待後車。"
文子曰："吾嘗好音，此人遺我鳴琴。吾好
佩，此人遺我玉環。是振我過者也。以求容於
我者，吾恐其以我求容於人也。"乃去之，果
收文子後車二乘，而獻之其君矣。

《韓非子·說林下》

42 Friend or Foe?

When Zhonghang Wenzi of the state of Jin became a fugitive he passed a certain county.

"The magistrate of this place is an old friend of yours," said his attendants. "Why don't you stay here and rest a bit while waiting for the carriages that are coming behind us?"

"At one time when I was fond of music," replied Wenzi, "this man gave me a beautifully tuned *qin* (a stringed instrument). There was another time when I became fond of jade ornaments; then he gave me jade rings. He was ready to abet me in my wrongdoings. Since he put himself out to win my favour, I am afraid that he will use me to win someone else's favour."

Thus Wenzi departed. It turned out that the magistrate did stop two carriages that came after Wenzi and offered them as a gift to his new master.

Hanfeizi

四十三　侏儒夢竈

　　衞靈公之時，彌子瑕有寵，專於衞國。侏
儒有見公者，曰：“臣之夢踐矣。”公曰：
“何夢？”對曰：“夢見竈，爲見公也。”公怒
曰：“吾聞見人主者夢見日，奚爲見寡人而夢
見竈？”對曰：“夫日兼燭天下，一物不能當
也。人君兼燭一國，一人不能擁也，故將見人
主者夢見日。夫竈，一人煬焉，則後人無從見
矣。今或者一人有煬君者乎？則臣雖夢見竈，
不亦可乎？”

《韓非子‧內儲說上》

43   A Dream Come True

When Duke Ling was ruling over the state of Wei, Mi Zixia, the duke's favourite minister, wielded absolute power in the state.

A dwarf came to see the duke.

"My lord," said the dwarf, "my dream has come true."

"What dream did you have?" asked the duke.

"In my dream I saw a kitchen stove, which means I will see my lord," replied the dwarf.

The duke was enraged. "I have heard that those who get to see their sovereign will dream of the sun. Why do you say that dreaming of a kitchen stove meant you will get to see me?"

"The sun," the dwarf replied, "shines over all the earth and no single object can block its light. The sovereign of a state sees all that goes on in his country and no single man can block his view. That is why seeing the sun in a dream means one gets to see the sovereign. As for a kitchen stove, when one person stands in front of it warming himself, no one behind him gets to see the light. Now perhaps there is someone who is doing just that to you, my lord. Then is it not understandable that I dreamed of a kitchen stove?"

Hanfeizi

四十四　南郭吹竽

　　齊宣王使人吹竽，必三百人。南郭處士請
爲王吹竽，宣王說之，廩食以數百人。
　　宣王死，湣王立，好一一聽之，處士逃。

《韓非子·內儲說上》

44 Safety in Numbers

Whenever King Xuan of the state of Qi ordered musicians to play the *yu*, an ancient wind instrument consisting of reed pipes, he insisted on three hundred musicians playing together. Nanguo, an educated man in retirement, asked permission to play the *yu* for the king. The king graciously gave his consent and Nanguo received the same salary as the other several hundred musicians.

After the death of King Xuan, King Min became the ruler of Qi. He liked to listen to the musicians one by one. Nanguo fled.

Hanfeizi

四十五　夫妻祝禱

　　衞人有夫妻禱者，而祝曰：“使我無故得百束布。”其夫曰：“何少也？”對曰：“益是，子將以買妾。”

《韓非子・內儲說下》

45   Earnest Prayers

In the state of Wei a couple was praying to the gods.

"Please let me have one hundred strings of cash without having to work for it," prayed the wife.

"Why so little?" asked her husband.

"If we have more," came her reply, "you'd go and get a concubine."

Hanfeizi

四十六　買櫝還珠

　　楚人有賣其珠於鄭者，爲木蘭之櫃，薰以桂椒，綴以珠玉，飾以玫瑰，輯以羽翠。鄭人買其櫝而還其珠。

　　此可謂善賣櫝矣，未可謂善鬻珠也。

《韓非子·外儲說左上》

46   The Casket and the Pearl

A man from the state of Chu wanted to sell a precious pearl in the state of Zheng. He made a casket for the pearl out of the wood from a magnolia tree, which he fumigated with fragrant osmanthus and spices. He studded the casket with pearls and jade, ornamented it with red gems and decorated it with kingfisher feathers. A man of the state of Zheng bought the casket and gave him back the pearl.

This man from Chu certainly knew how to sell a casket but he was no good at selling his pearl.

Hanfeizi

四十七　畫孰最難

　　客有爲齊王畫者。齊王問曰：“畫孰最難
者？”曰：“犬馬最難。”“孰易者？”曰：“鬼
魅最易。夫犬馬，人所知也，旦暮罄於前，不
可類之，故難；鬼魅，無形者，不罄於前，故
易之也。”

《韓非子·外儲說左上》

47   Ghost Drawing

The king of the state of Qi asked his guest who was drawing a picture for him, "What is most difficult to draw?"

"Dogs and horses are the most difficult."

"What is the easiest?"

"Ghosts are the easiest. Dogs and horses are familiar sights that we behold from morning till evening and it is not easy to capture the likeness. That is why they are so difficult to draw. As for ghosts, they have no shape and they do not appear before us. That is why it's so easy to draw them."

Hanfeizi

四十八　卜妻縫褲

鄭縣人卜子，使其妻爲袴。其妻問曰：
“今袴何如？”夫曰：“象吾故袴。”妻因毀
新令如故袴。

《韓非子·外儲說左上》

48   Good as Old

Buzi, a man of the county of Zheng, told his wife to make him a new pair of trousers.

"What do you want the new pair to be like?" asked his wife.

"Same as my old pair," he replied.

As a result, his wife ruined the new trousers to make them look exactly like the old pair.

Hanfeizi

四十九　鄭人買履

　　鄭人有欲買履者，先自度其足而置之其坐。至之市而忘操之。已得履，乃曰："吾忘持度。"反歸取之，及反，市罷，遂不得履。人曰："何不試之以足？"曰："寧信度，無自信也。"

《韓非子・外儲說左上》

49 Buying Shoes

A man of the state of Zheng wanted to buy a pair of shoes. He measured his foot and put the measurement on a chair. When he set out for the market he forgot to bring it along. It was after he had found the pair he wanted that this occurred to him.

"I forgot the measurement," said he.

He went home to get it but when he returned the market had broken up and he did not get his shoes after all.

"Why didn't you try on the shoes with your feet?" he was asked.

"I'd rather trust the measurement than trust myself."

Hanfeizi

五十　曾子殺猪

　　曾子之妻之市，其子隨之而泣。其母曰：
"女還，顧反爲女殺彘。"

　　妻適市來，曾子欲捕彘殺之，妻止之曰：
"特與嬰兒戲耳。"曾子曰："嬰兒非與戲也。
嬰兒非有知也，待父母而學者也，聽父母之敎。
今子欺之，是敎子欺也。母欺子，子而不信其
母，非以成敎也。"遂烹彘也。

《韓非子·外儲說左上》

50   An Example to Follow

As Zengzi's wife set off for the market, her little son followed her, crying.

"Go home," she said to the boy, "when I come back, I'll kill the pig for you to eat."

When she got back from the market Zengzi wanted to catch the pig and kill it.

His wife stopped him. "I was just humouring the child."

"Children cannot be humoured in this way," he replied. "They have little understanding. They learn from their parents and listen to what their parents teach them. By deceiving him now you are teaching him to deceive. If a mother deceives her son, her son would not believe his mother any more. This is not the way to teach a child." So he killed the pig and cooked it.

Hanfeizi

Zengzi: i.e. Zeng Shen

五十一　自相矛盾

　　楚人有鬻楯與矛者，譽之曰：“吾楯之堅，物莫能陷也。”又譽其矛曰：“吾矛之利，於物無不陷也。”或曰：“以子之矛，陷子之楯，何如？”其人弗能應也。夫不可陷之楯與無不陷之矛，不可同世而立。

《韓非子·難一》

51 His Spear Against His Shield

A man of the state of Chu had a spear and a shield for sale. He was loud in praises of his shield.

"My shield is so strong that nothing can pierce it through."

He also sang praises of his spear.

"My spear is so strong that it can pierce through anything."

"What would happen," he was asked, "if your spear is used to pierce your shield?"

He was unable to give an answer.

It is impossible for an impenetrable shield to coexist with a spear that finds nothing impenetrable.

Hanfeizi

五十二　守株待兔

宋人有耕者，田中有株，兔走觸株，折頸
而死。因釋其耒而守株，冀復得兔。兔不可復
得，而身為宋國笑。

《韓非子・五蠹》

52   The Vigil by the Tree Stump

In the state of Song there was a farmer in whose fields stood a tree stump. A hare which was running very fast dashed against the stump and died, having broken its neck. So the farmer abandoned his plough and waited by the tree stump, hoping to get another hare. He did not get his hare but became a laughing-stock in the state of Song.

Hanfeizi

五十三　祁黃羊擧賢

晉平公問於祁黃羊曰："南陽無令，其誰可而爲之？"祁黃羊對曰："解狐可。"平公曰："解狐非子之讎邪？"對曰："君問可，非問臣之讎也。"平公曰："善。"遂用之，國人稱善焉。

居有閒，平公又問祁黃羊曰："國無尉，其誰可而爲之？"對曰："午可。"平公曰："午非子之子邪？"對曰："君問可，非問臣之子也。"平公曰："善。"又遂用之，國人稱善焉。

孔子聞之曰："善哉祁黃羊之論也。外擧不避讎，內擧不避子。祁黃羊可謂公矣。"

《呂氏春秋·去私》

53 Recommendations

Duke Ping of the state of Jin asked Qi Huangyang, "There is a vacancy for a county magistrate in Nanyang. Who do you think is suitable for the post?"

"Xie Hu is a suitable candidate," replied Qi.

"Isn't Xie Hu your enemy?" asked the duke.

"My lord, you asked me who would be suitable for the post, not who my enemy was," came the reply.

"Good," said the duke.

Xie Hu was given the job and everyone in the state applauded the appointment.

After a short time, the duke asked Qi again, "The capital city needs a military official. Who do you think is suitable for the post?"

"Qi Wu is a suitable candidate," replied Qi.

"Isn't Qi Wu your son?" asked the duke.

"My lord, you asked me who would be suitable for the post, not who my son was," came the reply.

"Good," said the duke.

Qi Wu was also given the post and everyone in the state approved the appointment.

When Confucius got to know of this, he said, "Qi Huangyang's judgment is commendable indeed. When recommending one outside his family he did not discriminate against his enemy. When recommending a member of his family he had no scruples about choosing his own son. This is indeed a just and impartial man."

Lüshi chunqiu (Historical Writings Compiled by Lü Buwei)

五十四　列子學射

　　子列子常射中矣，請之於關尹子。關尹子曰：“知子之所以中乎？”答曰：“弗知也。”關尹子曰：“未可。”

　　退而習之三年，又請。關尹子曰：“子知子之所以中乎？”列子曰：“知之矣。”關尹子曰：“可矣，守而勿失。”

　　非獨射也，國之存也，國之亡也，身之賢也，身之不肖也，亦皆有以。

《呂氏春秋·審己》

54 How and Why

Liezi often managed to hit the bull's eye when shooting with his bow and arrows. Once he asked the advice of Guan Yinzi.

"Do you know why you could hit the bull's eye?" asked Guan Yinzi.

"No, I don't," replied Liezi.

"Then you still have much to learn."

Liezi returned home and practised his archery for three years before going once more to ask the advice of Guan Yinzi.

"Do you know why you could hit the bull's eye?" asked Guan Yinzi.

"Yes, I do," replied Liezi.

"Then you have succeeded. Make sure you do not forget what you have learned."

This does not only apply to archery. The rise and fall of nations, the virtues and vices of men all have reasons behind them.

Lüshi chunqiu (Historical Writings
Compiled by Lü Buwei)

五十五　孔子馬逸

孔子行道而息，馬逸。食人之稼，野人取其馬。子貢請往說之，畢辭，野人不聽。

有鄙人始事孔子者，曰：“請往說之。”因爲野人曰：“子不耕於東海，吾不耕於西海也。吾馬何得不食子之禾？”其野人大說，相謂曰：“說亦皆如此其辯也，獨如嚮之人！”解馬而與之。

《呂氏春秋·必己》

55 Powers of Persuasion

During one of his travels, Confucius was taking a rest when his horse ran away and ate a farmer's crops. The farmer would not let the horse go. Confucius' pupil Zigong, skilled in powers of persuasion, volunteered to go and talk to him. He made a moving speech but the farmer did not heed his words.

A rough fellow who had just followed Confucius for a short time said, "Please let me go and talk to him."

He said to the farmer, "You do not farm near the East Sea and we do not have farms near the West Sea. Here in the west, what do you expect our horse to eat if it can't eat your crops?"

Upon hearing these words the farmer was delighted. He said, "Plain speaking! That's the way to talk. Not like that man just now."

The farmer released the horse and returned it to him.

Lüshi chunqiu (Historical Writings Compiled by Lü Buwei)

Zigong: i.e. Duanmu Ci

五十六 刻舟求劍

　　楚人有涉江者，其劍自舟中墜於水，遽契其舟，曰：“是吾劍之所從墜。”舟止，從其所契者入水求之。

　　舟已行矣，而劍不行。求劍若此，不亦惑乎？

《呂氏春秋·察今》

56   Making His Mark

A man from the state of Chu was crossing a river. In the boat, his sword fell into the water. Immediately he made a mark on the boat.

"This is where my sword fell off," he said.

When the boat stopped moving, he went into the water to look for his sword at the place where he had marked the boat.

The boat had moved but the sword had not. Is this not a very foolish way to look for a sword?

Lüshi chunqiu (Historical Writings
Compiled by Lü Buwei)

五十七　一鳴驚人

　　荆莊王立三年，不聽而好讔。成公賈入諫。王曰：“不穀禁諫者，今子諫何故？”對曰：“臣非敢諫也，願與君王讔也。”王曰：“胡不設不穀矣？”對曰：“有鳥止於南方之阜，三年不動、不飛、不鳴，是何鳥也？”王射之曰：“有鳥止於南方之阜，其三年不動，將以定志意也；其不飛，將以長羽翼也；其不鳴，將以覽民則也。是鳥雖無飛，飛將衝天；雖無鳴，鳴將駭人。賈出矣，不穀知之矣。”明日朝，所進者五人，所退者十人。羣臣大說，荆國之眾相賀也。

《呂氏春秋·重言》

57   The Silent Bird

King Zhuang of the state of Chu had ruled the state for three years. He did not like to listen to the advice of his ministers but preferred solving riddles. Cheng Gonggu went to see the king with the intention of admonishing him.

"I do not permit admonitions from ministers," said the king. "So why are you here to admonish me?"

"Your majesty, I am not so bold as to admonish you for anything," replied Cheng. "I am here to solve riddles with you."

"Why not give me a riddle then," said the king.

"A certain bird rested on a hill in the south. For three years it did not move or fly or cry. What bird is that?"

The king solved the riddle. "This bird rested on a hill in the south. For three years it did not move because it wanted to strengthen its will and determination; it did not fly because it wanted to be fully-fledged; it did not cry because it wanted to observe the behaviour of the people. Though this bird does not fly, it will soar up the skies once it stretches its wings for flight. Though it does not cry, it will startle people once it opens its mouth to utter a sound. You may leave now. I understand what you are trying to say."

The next day when the king held court, he promoted five ministers and demoted ten others. All the ministers were delighted and the people in the state congratulated one another for having such a king.

Lüshi chunqiu (Historical Writings
Compiled by Lü Buwei)

五十八 掣 肘

宓子賤治亶父，恐魯君之聽讒人而令己不得行其術也。將辭而行，請近吏二人於魯君，與之俱至於亶父。

邑吏皆朝，宓子賤令吏二人書。吏方將書，宓子賤從旁時掣搖其肘，吏書之不善，則宓子賤為之怒。吏甚患之，辭而請歸。宓子賤曰："子之書甚不善，子勉歸矣。"

二吏歸報於君，曰："宓子不得為書。"君曰："何故？"吏對曰："宓子使臣書，而時掣搖臣之肘，書惡而有甚怒，吏皆笑宓子。此臣所以辭而去也。"

魯君太息而歎曰："宓子以此諫寡人之不肖也。寡人之亂子而令宓子不得行其術，必數有之矣。微二人，寡人幾過。"遂發所愛而令之亶父，告宓子曰："自今以來，亶父非寡人之有也，子之有也。有便於亶父者，子決為之

58   A Hand under the Elbow

Fu Zijian was appointed the governer of Danfu, a county in the state of Lu. He was afraid that the king of Lu would listen to malicious talk and hinder him from carrying out his policies. Before he set out to take up the post he asked the king to send two trusted officers to accompany him to Danfu.

All the officials of Danfu came to pay their respects. Fu Zijian told the two officers to make a record. When they were about to write Fu Zijian time and again went to their side and tugged at their elbows. Consequently the officers did not make a good job of writing and Fu Zijian was angry. The two of them were very annoyed and asked permission to take their leave.

"You are no good at writing," said Fu Zijian, "you had better hurry home."

The two officers reported back to the king. "We could not do any writing for Fu Zijian."

"How come?" asked the king.

"Fu Zijian told us to write but time and again he tugged at our elbows. When we did not write well he became angry. All the officials laughed at him. That is why we asked to leave."

The king heaved a sigh. "Fu Zijian did this to point out my error. I must have given him trouble and hindered the carrying out of his policies à number of times. If it was not for you two, I would have made a big mistake."

As a result, the king dispatched a trusted minister to Danfu and gave Fu Zijian a message: "From now on Danfu does not belong to me, it belongs to you. If anything can benefit Danfu, you make the decision. You only need to give me a concise report in five

矣，五歲而言其要。"宓子敬諾，乃得行其術
於亶父。

《呂氏春秋·具備》

years."

Fu Zijian respectfully accepted the king's trust and he managed to carry out his policies in Danfu.

Lüshi chunqiu (Historical Writings Compiled by Lü Buwei)

五十九　穿井得一人

　　宋之丁氏，家無井，而出溉汲，常一人居外。及其家穿井，告人曰：“吾穿井得一人。”

　　有聞而傳之者曰：“丁氏穿井得一人。”國人道之，聞之於宋君，宋君令人問之於丁氏。

　　丁氏對曰：“得一人之使，非得一人於井中也。”

《呂氏春秋·察傳》

59   Dig a Well and Get a Man

In the state of Song, a man named Ding had no well in his house, so water had to be obtained from outside and one servant was constantly out of the house to do this chore. When a well was dug in his house, Ding remarked, "I dug a well and got a man."

Some who heard this remark spread the news, "Ding dug a well and got a man."

It was talked about in the capital and the king of Song came to hear of it. The king sent someone to the Ding family to make enquiries.

"I meant I got an extra man to do my work," said Ding, "not getting a man out of the well."

Lüshi chunqiu (Historical Writings
Compiled by Lü Buwei)

六十　掩耳盜鐘

范氏之亡也，百姓有得鐘者，欲負而走，則鐘大不可負。以椎毀之，鐘況然有音。恐人聞之而奪己也，遽揜其耳。

惡人聞之，可也；惡己自聞之，悖矣。

《呂氏春秋·自知》

60 Ostrich Logic

At the time when Fan, a nobleman of the state of Jin, became a fugitive, a commoner found a bell and wanted to carry it off on his back. But the bell was too big for him. When he tried to knock it into pieces with a hammer there was a loud clanging sound. He was afraid that someone will hear the noise and take the bell from him, so he immediately stopped his own ears.

To worry about other people hearing the noise is understandable, but to worry about himself hearing the noise (as if stopping his own ears would prevent other people from hearing) is absurd.

Lüshi chunqiu (Historical Writings
Compiled by Lü Buwei)

六十一　二桃殺三士

公孫接、田開疆、古冶子事景公，以勇力搏虎聞。

晏子過而趨，三子者不起。晏子入見公曰：「臣聞明君之蓄勇力之士也，上有君臣之義，下有長率之倫，內可以禁暴，外可以威敵，上利其功，下服其勇，故尊其位，重其祿。今君之蓄勇力之士也；上無君臣之義，下無長率之倫，內不可以禁暴，外不可以威敵。此危國之器也，不若去之。」公曰：「三子者，搏之恐不得，刺之恐不中也。」晏子曰：「此皆力攻勍敵之人也，無長幼之禮。」因請公使人少餽之二桃，曰：「三子何不計功而食桃。」

61 Two Peaches for Three

Gongsun Jie, Tian Kaijiang and Gu Yezi, well known for their strength and courage which could even subdue a tiger, all served under Duke Jing of the state of Qi.

Once when the prime minister Yanzi came near the trio, he politely quickened his steps, but they took no notice of him and did not rise.

Yanzi went to see the duke.

"My lord," said Yanzi, "I have heard that when wise sovereigns keep brave men in their service, these men understood that to their lord, they must give their full allegiance, while to their elders, they must show due respect; they can suppress riots from within, and overcome enemies that attack from without. Those on high appreciate their achievements and the lowly admire their courage. That is why they occupy exalted positions and receive large salaries. My lord, the brave men that are now in your service know nothing about giving full allegiance to their lord or showing due respect to their elders. They are unable to suppress riots from within or overcome enemies from without. They are a menace to our state and we should get rid of them."

"These three men," said the duke, "cannot be easily overpowered and not even an assassin has a good chance of killing them."

"They only know how to fight with strong enemies," pointed out Yanzi. "They know nothing about giving precedence to elders."

He then asked the duke to send a messenger to the three men presenting them with two peaches and a

公孫接仰天而歎曰："晏子，智人也。夫使公之計吾功者。不受桃，是無勇也。士眾而桃寡，何不計功而食桃矣！接一搏特猏，再搏乳虎。若接之功，可以食桃，而無與人同矣。"援桃而起。田開疆曰："吾仗兵而却三軍者再。若開疆之功，亦可以食桃，而無與人同矣。"援桃而起。古冶子曰："吾嘗從君濟於河，黿銜左驂，以入砥柱之中流。當是時也，冶少不能游，潛行，逆流百步，順流九里，得黿而殺之。左操驂尾，右挈黿頭，鶴躍而出。津人皆曰：'河伯也。'視之則大黿之首也。若冶之功，亦可以食桃，而無與人同矣！二人何不反桃？"抽劍而起。公孫接、田開疆曰："吾勇

message: Divide the peaches among yourselves according to your achievements.

Gongsun Jie lifted his head and heaved a sigh. "Yanzi is indeed a clever man. He persuaded the duke to make us measure our own achievements. If we do not accept the peaches, it seems that we do not have courage. But there are so many of us and so few peaches. We have to divide them by weighing our own achievements. I first overcame a three-year-old wild boar, then I fought with a tigress that had just given birth to a litter. On the strength of my merits I am entitled to a peach and need not share it with anyone." He took a peach and rose.

"Twice with my weapons," said Tian Kaijiang, "I forced invading armies to retreat. Considering the service I rendered, I think I also deserve one peach and need not share it with anyone." He took a peach and rose.

"I once crossed the Yellow River with our lord," said Gu Yezi. "A big turtle gripped the carriage horse on the left with its teeth and dragged it into the rapid currents in the middle of the river. At that time it was impossible for me to swim so I had to go under the water. I went forward a hundred paces against the current and then went along with the current for nine *li* before I got hold of the turtle and killed it. With the tail of the horse in my left hand and the head of the big turtle in my right, I burst out of the water like a graceful crane. Whereupon all the people on the ferry cried, 'It is the god of the river.' When they took a closer look they saw that it was the head of the big turtle. On the strength of my achievements I also deserve to eat a peach without having to share it with anyone. Why don't the two of you give back the peaches." He rose,

不子若，功不子逮。取桃不讓，是貪也；然而不死，無勇也。"皆反其桃，挈領而死。古冶子曰："二子死之，冶獨生之，不仁；恥人以言，而夸其聲，不義；恨乎所行，不死，無勇。雖然二子同桃而節，冶專桃而宜。"亦反其桃，挈領而死。

使者復曰："已死矣。"公殮之以服，葬之以士禮焉。

《晏子春秋·內篇諫下》

drawing his sword out of its sheath.

"We are not as brave as you," said Gongsun Jie and Tian Kaijiang, "and our achievements cannot compare with yours. If we hold on to the peaches and refuse to let you have them, that is greed. But if we do not die, that shows we have no courage."

They surrendered the peaches and killed themselves by cutting their throats.

"If I alone live when they are dead, I am without honour. If I praise myself and hurt others with my words, I am unjust. If I regret what I did but do not die I am a coward — even though it is appropriate that they share a peach and I have one for myself." Gu relinquished his peach and cut his throat.

The messenger returned and said to the duke, "They are all dead."

The duke gave orders that they were to be put into coffins clothed in the proper garments and be given the funeral of a brave warrior.

Yanzi chunqiu (Historical Anecdotes of Yanzi)

Yanzi: i.e. Yan Ying

六十二　晏子車夫

　　晏子爲齊相，出，其御之妻，從門閒而闚其夫爲相御，擁大蓋，策駟馬，意氣揚揚，甚自得也。

　　旣而歸，其妻請去。夫問其故，妻曰：“晏子長不滿六尺，身相齊國，名顯諸侯。今者妾觀其出，志念深矣，常有以自下者。今子長八尺，迺爲人僕御。然子之意自以爲足。妾是以求去也。”

　　其後，夫自抑損。晏子怪而問之，御以實對。晏子薦以爲大夫。

《晏子春秋·內篇雜上》

62   The Driver of Yanzi's Carriage

Yanzi became the Prime Minister of the state of Qi. As he was going out, the wife of his carriage driver peeped out behind the door which was opened just a crack. She saw her husband drive the Prime Minister's carriage, sitting beneath the big canopy, cracking his whip at the team of four horses in front of him. He had a cocksure expression on his face and seemed very pleased with himself.

When the driver returned, his wife wanted a divorce. He asked for an explanation.

"Yanzi is not even six *chi* tall , " she pointed out. "He is the Prime Minister of Qi and enjoys a high reputation among the rulers of the different states. Today I watched him go out. He is a man of great depth but his bearing is so modest and unassuming. Now you are over eight *chi* tall and you are only a carriage driver. But you looked so cocky and puffed-up. That is why I want to leave you."

From then onwards the driver restrained himself and learned to be more modest. This surprised Yanzi. He questioned the driver who told him the truth. As a result Yanzi recommended him to the post of a senior officer of the state.

Yanzi chunqiu (Historical Anecdotes of Yanzi)

Chi: a Chinese unit of length equal to one fourth of a metre.

六十三　晏子使楚

　　晏子使楚。楚人以晏子短，爲小門于大門之側而延晏子。晏子不入，曰：“使狗國者，從狗門入。今臣使楚，不當從此門入。”儐者更道，從大門入。

　　見楚王，王曰：“齊無人耶？使子爲使。”

　　晏子對曰：“齊之臨淄三百閭，張袂成陰，揮汗成雨，比肩繼踵而在，何爲無人！”

　　王曰：“然則何爲使子？”

　　晏子對曰：“齊命使，各有所主。其賢者使使賢主，不肖者使使不肖主。嬰最不肖，故宜使楚矣。”

《晏子春秋・內篇雜下》

63   Each to His Own Kind

Yanzi came to the state of Chu as ambassador. The men of Chu knew him to be a short man so they specially opened a little door next to the main entrance and asked him to enter.

Yanzi refused. "An ambassador to a country of dogs would enter by the dog's door," he pointed out, "I am now ambassador to Chu and it is not right for me to enter by this door."

The men sent to receive him had to take him through the main door, instead of going the way they originally intended.

When Yanzi was in the presence of the king, the king asked him, "Is there no one in the state of Qi? Is that why you are sent to be the ambassador?"

"In Qi's capital city Linzi," replied Yanzi, "there are over seven thousand households. If everyone stretched out his sleeve, the sun would be blotted out. If everyone wiped his drops of perspiration, it would be like rain falling. Men in the streets had to rub shoulders with one another, their toes coming up against another's heels. How could there be no one in Qi?"

"Then why are you sent as ambassador?"

"In appointing ambassadors," replied Yanzi, "the state of Qi takes into account the sort of country one is sent to. Able men are sent to states with able rulers. Incompetent men are sent to states with incompetent rulers. I am the most incompetent of all, so I am sent to Chu."

Yanzi chunqiu (Historical Anecdotes of Yanzi)

六十四　橘化爲枳

晏子將使楚。楚王聞之，謂左右曰：“晏嬰，齊之習辭者也。今方來，吾欲辱之，何以也？”

左右對曰：“爲其來也，臣請縛一人，過王而行。王曰：‘何爲者也？’對曰：‘齊人也。’王曰：‘何坐？’曰：‘坐盜。’”

晏子至，楚王賜晏子酒。酒酣，吏二縛一人詣王，王曰：“縛者曷爲者也？”對曰：“齊人也，坐盜。”

王視晏子曰：“齊人固善盜乎？”

晏子避席對曰：“嬰聞之，橘生淮南，則爲橘，生於淮北，則爲枳。葉徒相似，其實味不同。所以然者何？水土異也。今民生長於齊不盜，入楚則盜。得無楚之水土，使民善盜耶？”

王笑曰：“聖人非所與熙也，寡人反取病焉。”

《晏子春秋·內篇雜下》

64   Oranges and Tangerines

Yanzi was soon to come to the state of Chu as ambassador.

When the king of Chu heard the news he said to his ministers, "In the state of Qi, Yan Ying is famed for his quick wit. Now he is coming to our state. I want to humiliate him. How should I do it?"

"When he comes," replied a minister, "please permit me to bind up a man and make him walk past you. Then your majesty will ask, 'What man is this?' And I will reply, 'This is a man from Qi.' Your majesty will ask again, 'What crime has he committed?' I will say, 'He is convicted of theft.'"

Yanzi arrived and the king gave a banquet in his honour. When everyone was merry with drink, two officers took a man in bonds before the king.

"Why is this man bound up?" asked the king.

"This is a man from Qi. He is a thief," came the reply.

The king looked at Yanzi. "Have the people of Qi always been good at stealing?"

Yanzi left his seat and replied respectfully, "I have heard that tangerine trees planted south of the River Huai produce tangerines but those planted north of the river produce oranges. The leaves of the two trees look alike but the fruits taste very different. What is the reason behind this? — the difference in natural environment and climate. Now men born and bred in Qi do not steal but when they come to Chu they become thieves. Could it be that the environment of Chu induces men to steal?"

The king laughed. "It is impossible to make fun of a learned and virtuous man. The joke is now on me."

Yanzi chunqiu (Historical Anecdotes of Yanzi)

六十五 陽　橋

宓子賤爲單父宰，過於陽晝曰："子亦有以送僕乎？"陽晝曰："吾少也賤，不知治民之術，有釣道二焉，請以送子。"子賤曰："釣道奈何？"陽晝曰："夫扱綸錯餌，迎而吸之者，陽橋也。其爲魚，薄而不美。若存若亡，若食若不食者，魴也，其爲魚，博而厚味。"子賤曰："善。"

未至單父，冠蓋迎之者交接於道。子賤曰："車驅之，車驅之！夫陽晝之所謂'陽橋'者至矣。"於是至單父，請其耆老尊賢者而與之共治單父。

《宓子》

65 Fishing Tips

When Fu Zijian was appointed magistrate of the Danfu county he paid Yang Zhou a visit.

"Sir," said Fu Zijian, "do you have any advice to give me?"

"All my life," said Yang Zhou, "I have occupied a lowly position and I know little about governing people. But there are two things about fishing I would like you to accept as a present form me."

"What about fishing?" asked Fu Zijian.

"When you drop your line with the bait in place and a fish immediately comes forward to swallow it, that fish is sure to be a *yangqiao* which has very little flesh and is not tasty at all. A fish that seems to be there and then disappears; a fish that seems to swallow the bait and then lets go of it — that is the bream which has a lot of flesh and is extremely tasty."

"Sir, your advice is excellent," said Fu Zijian.

Before Fu Zijian reached Danfu he was met on the way by a lot of officials garbed in splendid robes, sitting in canopied carriages.

"Get going, get going," Fu Zijian urged his servants, "the *yangqiao* Yang Zhou told me about have shown up."

When he reached Danfu, he respectfully invited wise old men who were highly esteemed to govern the county together with him.

Fuzi

六十六　宓子賤與巫馬期

宓子賤治單父，彈鳴琴，身不下堂，而單父治。巫馬期亦治單父，以星出，以星入，日夜不處，以身親之，而單父亦治。

巫馬期問其故於宓子。宓子曰："我之謂任人，子之謂任力。任力者固勞，任人者固佚。"

《景子》

66 Leisure and Exhaustion

When Fu Zijian governed the county of Danfu, he often played his *qin,* a stringed instrument, and seldom went out. The whole county benefited from his rule. Wu Maqi also governed Danfu for a period of time. He went out before the stars disappeared from the sky and did not return until the stars came out. He had little rest day or night, taking care of everything himself. The county also benefited under his rule.

Wu Maqi asked Fu Zijian why this was so.

"My way," said Fu Zijian, "is to make people work for me. Your way is to rely on your own strength. It naturally follows that relying on your own strength results in exhaustion while making others work for you results in leisure."

Jingzi

六十七　楚人兩妻

　　楚人有兩妻者，人挑其長者，詈之，挑其少者，少者許之。

　　居無幾何，有兩妻者死。客謂挑者曰：“汝取長者乎，少者乎？”“取長者。”客曰：“長者詈汝，少者和汝。汝何爲取長者？”曰：“居彼人之所，則欲其許我也，今爲我妻，則欲其爲我詈人也。”

《戰國策·秦策一》

67 A Different Time, a Different Need

A man of the state of Chu had two wives. Someone made a pass at the older wife but was rebuked by her. When he did the same to the younger woman she did not repulse him.

After a short time, this man with the two wives died.

The one who had made passes at the ladies was asked, "Which do you want to marry, the older or the younger?"

"The older," came the reply.

"The older one rebuked you but the younger accepted your advances. Why do you want to marry the older lady?"

"When I was staying in another man's house, of course I liked the one that yielded to me. Now that I want a wife, I want one that would rebuke men who try to get fresh with her."

Zhanguo ce (Strategies of the
Warring States)

六十八　管莊刺虎

　　有兩虎諍人而鬥者，管莊子將刺之。

　　管與止之曰：“虎者，戾蟲；人者，甘餌
也。今兩虎諍人而鬥，小者必死，大者必傷。
子待傷虎而刺之，則是一舉而兼兩虎也。無刺
一虎之勞，而有刺兩虎之名。”

《戰國策·秦策二》

68   It Pays to Wait

Two tigers were fighting over a man. Guan Zhuang-zi was about to stab the beasts.

Guan Yu stopped him.   "Tigers are greedy and ferocious beasts and man is delicious food for them. Now two tigers are fighting over a man. The smaller tiger is sure to die and the larger will certainly be wounded. Wait till the tiger is wounded before stabbing it. With one blow you will get two tigers. Then you would have been spared the trouble of killing one tiger while getting the credit for putting two tigers to death."

Zhanguo ce (Strategies of the
Warring States)

六十九　扁鵲之言

　　　　醫扁鵲見秦武王。武王示之病，扁鵲請
除。

　　　　左右曰：“君之病，在耳之前，目之下，
除之未必已也，將使耳不聰，目不明。”

　　　　君以告扁鵲。

　　　　扁鵲怒而投其石，曰：“君與知之者謀之，
而與不知之者敗之。使此知秦國之政也，則君
一舉而亡國矣！”

《戰國策·秦策二》

69   Choice of Counsellors

Doctor Bianque , a famous physician, came to see King Wu of the state of Qin. The king told the doctor about his condition and Bianque was ready to give him treatment.

The ministers at the king's side said to him, "Sire, your malady is in front of your ears and below your eyes. Even with treatment it might not be cured and very likely you will lose your hearing and your sight."

The king related these words to Bianque.

Bianque was enraged and threw down the stone needle which he used for giving treatment.

"Sire, you discuss your illness with one who knows how to effect a cure but you allow those who know nothing about medicine to spoil the whole thing. If Qin is governed in this way, then one such mistake on your part is enough to bring down the state."

Zhanguo ce (Strategies of the Warring States)

Bianque: i.e. Qin Yueren

七十　曾參殺人

　　昔者曾子處費。費人有與曾子同名族者而殺人。人告曾子母曰：“曾參殺人。”曾子之母曰：“吾子不殺人。”織自若。有頃焉，人又曰：“曾參殺人。”其母尚織自若也。頃之，一人又告之曰：“曾參殺人。”其母懼，投杼踰牆而走。

《戰國策·秦策二》

70 One Time Too Many

Zeng Shen once lived in a place called Mi. A man of Mi who had the same first and last names as Zeng Shen killed a man.

Someone told Zeng Shen's mother, "Zeng Shen killed a man."

"My son would not kill anybody," she said and continued weaving as she had always done.

After a while another man said, "Zeng Shen killed a man." She still went on weaving as before.

In a little while a third man came and said to her, "Zeng Shen has killed a man."

Zeng's mother became so frightened that she threw down her shuttle and fled over the wall.

Zhanguo ce (Strategies of the Warring States)

七十一　江上處女

　　夫江上之處女，有家貧而無燭者。處女相與語，欲去之。

　　家貧無燭者將去矣，謂處女曰：“妾以無燭故，常先至，掃室布席。何愛餘明之照四壁者？幸以賜妾，何妨於處女？妾自以有益於處女，何爲去我？”

　　處女相語，以爲然而留之。

《戰國策·秦策二》

71   The Maidens on the River Bank

On the river bank lived a number of maidens. One of them was very poor and could not afford a lamp. The others talked about it among themselves and wanted her to leave.

When the one who could not afford a lamp was about to go, she said to the other girls, "Because I have no lamp I am often here before you, cleaning up the place and getting the mats ready for you to sit on. Why do you grudge the little extra light that shines on these four walls? If you benefit me with a little light, what have you got to lose? I think I am of some use to you all. Why do you want me to go?"

The maidens discussed among themselves and admitted the force of her arguments. She was asked to stay.

Zhanguo ce (Strategies of the
Warring States)

七十二　鄒　忌

　　鄒忌修八尺有餘，身體昳麗。朝服衣冠，窺鏡，謂其妻曰：“我孰與城北徐公美？”其妻曰：“君美甚，徐公何能及公也！”城北徐公，齊國之美麗者也。忌不自信，而復問其妾曰：“吾孰與徐公美？”妾曰：“徐公何能及君也！”旦日，客從外來，與坐談，問之客曰：“吾與徐公孰美？”客曰：“徐公不若君之美也。”明日，徐公來，孰視之，自以為不如；窺鏡而自視，又弗如遠甚。暮寢而思之，曰：“吾妻之美我者，私我也；妾之美我者，畏我也；客之美我者，欲有求於我也。”

《戰國策·齊策一》

72 Speaking the Truth

Zou Ji, the prime minister of the state of Qi, was over eight *chi* tall and extremely good looking. One morning after putting on his hat and clothes, he looked at himself in the mirror and asked his wife, "Who is the handsomer, Xu Gong who lives north of the city or I?"

"You are by far the handsomer. How could Xu Gong compare with you?" answered his wife.

Xu Gong, who lived north of the city, was famous in Qi for his good looks. Zou Ji himself was not convinced so he put forward his question again, this time to his concubine.

"Who is handsomer, Xu Gong or I?"

"How could Xu Gong compare with you?" said his concubine.

The following day a man came to visit Zou. Zou sat with his guest and after chatting for a while, he asked, "Who do you think is handsomer, Xu Gong or I?"

"Xu Gong is not as handsome as you," replied his visitor.

Another day passed. Xu Gong came for a visit and Zou, looking at him most carefully, came to the conclusion that he himself was not as good looking. After inspecting his own reflection in the mirror, he felt that he could not hold a candle to Xu Gong in looks.

When night came, Zou pondered over the matter in bed, "My wife said I am better looking because she has a partiality for me. My concubine said I am better looking because she is afraid of me. My guest said I am better looking because he had a favour to ask of me."

Zhanguo ce (Strategies of the Warring States)

七十三　畫蛇添足

　　楚有祠者，賜其舍人卮酒。舍人相謂曰：
"數人飲之不足，一人飲之有餘，請畫地爲蛇，
先成者飲酒。"

　　一人蛇先成，引酒且飲之，乃左手持卮，
右手畫蛇，曰："吾能爲之足。"未成，一人
之蛇成，奪其卮曰："蛇固無足，子安能爲之
足？"遂飲其酒，爲蛇足者，終亡其酒。

《戰國策・齊策二》

73   The 'Finishing' Touch

In the state of Chu, an aristocrat, after offering
sacrifices to his ancestors, bestowed a flask of wine
on the gentlemen who worked for him. They discussed
among themselves.

"The wine is not enough for several and too much
for one person. Let us each draw a snake on the floor
and the first one that finishes his drawing drinks the
wine."

A man finished his drawing first. He took the wine
and was about to drink it when, with the flask in his
left hand, he drew with his right hand, saying, "I can
even add legs to my snake."

Before he finished, another man completed his
drawing and snatched the flask from him.

"A snake does not have legs. How could you add
legs to it?"

With these words he drank the wine. The one who
added legs to the snake eventually lost his wine.

Zhanguo ce (Strategies of the
Warring States)

七十四　狐假虎威

　　虎求百獸而食之，得狐。

　　狐曰：“子無敢食我也。天帝使我長百獸。今子食我，是逆天帝命也。子以我爲不信，吾爲子先行，子隨我後，觀百獸之見我而敢不走乎？”

　　虎以爲然，故遂與之行。獸見之皆走。虎不知獸畏己而走也，以爲畏狐也。

《戰國策·楚策一》

74   A Tiger in Tow

A tiger, on the hunt for animals to devour, caught a fox.

"You cannot be so bold as to eat me," said the fox, "I am sent by the heavenly god to rule over the animal kingdom.   If you eat me you will be going against a heavenly mandate.   Do you think I am lying?   Let me go first and you follow behind.   We'll see whether any animal is so brave as not to flee when they see me."

The tiger agreed to the plan and accordingly went with the fox.   All the animals who saw them fled. The tiger, under the impression that they were afraid of the fox, was unaware that he himself was the cause of their flight.

Zhanguo ce (Strategies of the
Warring States)

七十五　驚弓之鳥

　　更羸與魏王處京臺之下，仰見飛鳥，更羸
謂魏王曰：“臣爲王引弓虛發而下鳥。”魏王
曰：“然則射可至此乎？”更羸曰：“可。”

　　有間，雁從東方來，更羸以虛發而下之。
魏王曰：“然則射可至此乎？”更羸曰：“此
孽也。”王曰：“先生何以知之？”對曰：“其
飛徐而鳴悲。飛徐者，故瘡痛也，鳴悲者，久
失羣也。故瘡未息而驚心未至也，聞弦音引而
高飛，故瘡隕也。”

《戰國策・楚策四》

75 A Frightened Bird

Once upon a time, a skilled archer called Geng Lei and the king of the state of Wei were standing at the foot of a tall tower. Lifting their heads, they saw birds soaring in the sky.

"Sire, I can bring down a bird for you by using a bow with no arrow," said Geng to the king.

"Can the skills of archery achieve such a marvellous thing?" asked the king.

"Yes, sire," replied Geng.

After a little while, a wild goose appeared from the east, Geng merely drew his bow and brought down the bird.

"How come your skill can do such a wonderful thing?" asked the king.

"This is a wounded bird," said Geng.

"Sir, how do you know that?" asked the king.

"It was flying very slowly and crying very sadly," Geng pointed out. "It flew slowly because its old wound still hurt. It cried sadly because it had lost its flock for quite sometime. Its old wound had not yet healed and it was still very frightened. When it heard the sound of the bow it stretched its wings to soar up into the sky. That affected the wound and caused it to fall."

Zhanguo ce (Strategies of the Warring States)

七十六　南轅北轍

　　魏王欲攻邯鄲。季梁聞之，中道而反，衣焦不申，頭塵不去，往見王曰：“今者臣來，見人於大行，方北面而持其駕，告臣曰：‘我欲之楚。’臣曰：‘君之楚，將奚爲北面？’曰：‘吾馬良。’臣曰：‘馬雖良，此非楚之路也。’曰：‘吾用多。’臣曰：‘用雖多，此非楚之路也。’曰：‘吾御者善。’此數者愈善而離楚愈遠耳。今王動欲成霸王，舉欲信於天下；恃王國之大，兵之精銳，而攻邯鄲，以廣地尊名。王之動愈數，而離王愈遠耳。猶至楚而北行也。”

《戰國策・魏策四》

76   In the Opposite Direction

The king of the state of Wei had the intention of attacking Handan, capital of the state of Yue. Ji Liang, a minister of Wei, heard of this and broke off his journey to return to Wei. He went to see the king before even stopping to smooth the creases of his clothes or flick the dust off his head.

"Your majesty," said Ji Liang, "on my way here I saw a man at a main road driving his carriage which was facing north.

"He said to me, 'I want to go to the state of Chu.'

"'If you want to go to Chu, why are you going north?' I asked.

"'I have fine horses,' he said.

"'Even though you have good horses, this is not the road to Chu,' I pointed out.

"'I have plenty of money for my journey,' he said.

"'Even though you have a lot of money for your journey, this is not the road to Chu,' I said.

"'I have an excellent driver for my carriage,' he said.

"The better are the resources he mentioned, the further he was going from Chu.

"Now your majesty seeks to rise above all the kings and win the confidence and support of the common people everywhere. However, you plan to extend your territories and raise your prestige by attacking Handan, relying on the powerful strength of your state and the well-trained soldiers under your command. The more you move in this direction the further you are from your goal of ruling over all the states. This is as effective as going north hoping to reach the state of Chu."

Zhanguo ce (Strategies of the Warring States)

七十七 忠信致笞

有遠爲吏者，其妻私人。其夫且歸，其私之者憂之。其妻曰："公勿憂也。吾已爲藥酒以待之矣。"後二日，夫至。妻使妾奉卮酒進之。妾知其藥酒也，進之則殺主父，言之則逐主母。乃陽僵棄酒。主父大怒而笞之。

故妾一僵而棄酒，上以活主父，下以存主母也，忠至如此，然不免於笞。此以忠信得罪者也。

《戰國策·燕策一》

77   A Case of Injustice

A man held an official post far away from home.
His wife had an affair with another man. When the
husband's return drew near, her lover became very
worried.

"Don't worry," said the woman, "I have poisoned
wine waiting for him."

Two days later, the husband returned. The wife
told the concubine to take a cup of wine to him. The
concubine knew there was poison in the wine. If she
took in the wine her master would be killed; if she
revealed the plot, her mistress would be sent away.
So she pretended to trip and spilled the wine. Her
master flew into a rage and gave her a beating.

In pretending to trip and spilling the wine, the
concubine not only saved her master's life but also
preserved her mistress's position. But even such loyalty
brought on a beating. This is a case of getting punished
for being loyal.

Zhanguo ce (Strategies of the
Warring States)

七十八　求千里馬

　　古之君人，有以千金求千里馬者，三年不能得。

　　涓人言於君曰：“請求之。”君遣之。三月得千里馬。馬已死，買其首五百金，反以報君。君大怒曰：“所求者生馬，安事死馬而捐五百金？”涓人對曰：“死馬且買之五百金，況生馬乎？天下必以王爲能市馬，馬今至矣。”

　　於是不能期年，千里之馬至者三。

《戰國策・燕策一》

78 An Expensive Head

In the ancient times there was a king who wanted to find a swift horse that could cover a thousand *li* in one day and he was willing to pay one thousand pieces of gold. But for three years he was unsuccessful.

A eunuch said to the king, "Please let me go and find such a horse for you."

The king agreed to send him. After three months the eunuch found a very swift horse but it was dead. He bought the horse's head for five hundred pieces of gold and returned to report to the king.

"I want a living horse," fumed the king. "What is the use of a dead one? And you gave away five hundred gold pieces as well!"

"If a dead horse is worth five hundred gold pieces," answered the eunuch, "what would a live one be worth? People everywhere will know that the king is willing to pay a great deal to buy horses. Good horses will soon appear."

In less than a year, three fine horses very swift of foot were brought to the king.

Zhanguo ce (Strategies of the Warring States)

七十九　賣駿馬

　　人有賣駿馬者，比三旦立市，人莫之知。往見伯樂曰：“臣有駿馬，欲賣之，比三旦立於市，人莫與言。願子還而視之，去而顧之。臣請獻一朝之賈。”

　　伯樂乃還而視之，去而顧之。一旦而馬價十倍。

《戰國策・燕策二》

79   To Sell a Horse

A man wanted to sell a very fine horse. He stood in the market with his horse for three mornings but no one noticed that his horse was an exceptionally good one. He went to see Bo Le who was well-known for his ability to judge horses.

"Sir, I have a very fine horse for sale," he said, "but I stood in the market with my horse for three mornings and no one even spoke to me. Could you kindly come and look at my horse, walk all round it and throw a backward glance at it before you leave? I will pay you one day's wages."

So Bo Le went to look at the horse, walked all round it and threw a backward glance at it before he left. Immediately the price of the horse increased tenfold.

Zhanguo ce (Strategies of the Warring States)

八十 鷸蚌相爭

蚌方出曝，而鷸啄其肉。蚌合而拑其喙。

鷸曰：“今日不雨，明日不雨，即有死蚌。”

蚌亦謂鷸曰：“今日不出，明日不出，即有死鷸。”

兩者不肯相舍，漁者得而并禽之。

《戰國策·燕策二》

80   The Snipe and the Clam

Just as a clam came out to bask in the sun a snipe pecked at its flesh. The clam closed its shell and gripped the snipe's beak.

"If it does not rain today and it does not rain tomorrow, you will be a dead clam," said the snipe.

"If you cannot free yourself today and you cannot free yourself tomorrow, you will be a dead snipe," replied the clam.

Neither one would give way and eventually a fisherman caught both the clam and the snipe.

Zhanguo ce (Strategies of the Warring States)

八十一　相人之友

楚有善相人者，所言無遺，美聞於國中。莊王召見而問焉，對曰：「臣非能相人也，能相人之友者也。」

《韓詩外傳》

81 Telling Company

In the state of Chu was a man skilled in physiognomy. His comments were very accurate and his fame spread through the state. King Zhuang sent for him and asked him the secret of his success.

"Sire," said the man, "I am not good at judging character or telling fortunes by examining a person's face. I arrive at my conclusions through observing a person's friends."

Hanshi waizhuan (Han Ying's Illustration of the Didactic Application of the Book of Songs)

八十二　屠牛吐之智

　　齊王厚送女，欲妻屠牛吐。屠牛吐辭之以疾。其友曰："子終死腥臭之肆而已乎，何爲辭之？"吐應之曰："其女醜。"其友曰："子何知之？"吐曰："以吾屠知之。"其友曰："何謂也？"吐曰："吾肉善，如量而去，苦少耳；吾肉不善，雖以吾附益之，尚猶賈不售。今厚送子，子醜故耳。"其友後見之，果醜。

《韓詩外傳》

82   The Shrewdness of Tu the Butcher

The king of the state of Qi prepared a large dowry for his daughter and wanted Tu the butcher to marry her. Tu declined on the grounds that he was ill.

"You will only end your days in that stinking shop," pointed out his friend. "Why did you turn down the match?"

"The king's daughter is very plain," replied Tu.

"How do you know?" asked his friend.

"From my experience as a butcher," said Tu.

"What do you mean?" asked his friend.

"When the meat I sell is good," said Tu, "I just give the customer the amount he asks for and I still do not have enough meat to satisfy the demand. When the meat is not good, a lot of it is left on my hands even if I give the customers something extra for every piece they buy. Now the king has prepared a large dowry. The reason must be that his daughter is very homely."

Tu's friend did get to see the king's daughter. She really did turn out to be a very plain girl.

Hanshi waizhuan (Han Ying's Illustration of the Didactic Application of the Book of Songs)

八十三　苛政比虎

　　孔子過泰山側，有婦人哭於墓者而哀。夫子式而聽之，使子路問之曰：“子之哭也，壹似重有憂者。”而曰：“然。昔者，吾舅死於虎，吾夫又死焉，今吾子又死焉。”夫子曰：“何爲不去也？”曰：“無苛政。”夫子曰：“小子識之，苛政猛於虎也。”

《禮記·檀弓下》

83 More Threatening than Tigers

As Confucius was passing near Tai Mountain, he saw a woman weeping bitterly in front of a grave. He leaned forward to listen, resting his hand on the wooden bar of his carriage. Zilu , his pupil , was sent to ask the woman what the matter was.

"From your weeping it seems that you have many sorrows."

"That is true. In the past my father-in-law was killed by a tiger. My husband was also killed by a tiger. Now my son too is killed."

"Then why don't you leave this place?" asked Confucius.

"There is no tyrannical government here," came the reply.

"Take note, all of you," said Confucius, "a tyrannical government is more threatening than tigers."

Liji (The Book of Rites)

Zilu: i.e. Zhong You

八十四 嗟來之食

齊大饑。黔敖爲食於路，以待餓者而食之。

有餓者，蒙袂輯屨貿貿然來。黔敖左奉食右執飲曰："嗟，來食！"揚其目而視之，曰："予唯不食嗟來之食，以至於斯也。"從而謝焉，終不食而死。

《禮記·檀弓下》

84   A Matter of Dignity

There was a great famine in the state of Qi. Qian Ao, a rich man of Qi, prepared food by the roadside for the hungry to come and eat.

Along came a starving man, his sleeves covering his head, his hempen sandals held together by string, walking as if he did not know where he was going. With food in his left hand and drink in his right, Qian Ao shouted at him.

"Hey you! Come and eat!"

The man lifted his eyes and stared at Qian.

"I am reduced to this state just because I refuse to take anything from loud-mouthed people giving away food," he said.

Qian immediately begged his pardon but the man still refused to eat and eventually starved to death.

Liji (The Book of Rites)

八十五　哭母誇孝

　　　　東家母死，其子哭之不哀。西家子見之，
歸謂其母曰：“社何愛速死？吾必悲哭社。”
夫欲其母之死者，雖死亦不能悲哭矣。

《淮南子‧說山訓》

85 A Better Mourner

A family that lived in the eastern part of town was bereaved of the mother, but the son did not show any deep grief when weeping for her. The son of a family in the western part of town saw this and, on returning home, he said to his mother, "Ma, why are you so stingy about your life and not die sooner? If I were to mourn for you, I will weep most bitterly."

Those who wish for their mother's death would not shed tears of grief even if their mother did pass away.

Huainanzi

八十六　鬻母行義

　　郢人有鬻其母，爲請於買者曰：“此母老矣，幸善食之而勿苦。”此行大不義而欲爲小義者。

《淮南子・說山訓》

86 Mother for Sale

A native of Ying, capital of the state of Chu, sold his mother. He made entreaties for his mother to the one who bought her.

"My mother is old. Please see that she has enough food and do not ill-treat her."

This was an example of one who wanted to do a small good deed while indulging in a heinous act.

Huainanzi

八十七　塞翁失馬

　　近塞上之人，有善術者。馬無故亡而入胡，人皆弔之。其父曰："此何遽不爲福乎？"居數月，其馬將胡駿馬而歸，人皆賀之。其父曰："此何遽不能爲禍乎？"家富良馬，其子好騎，墮而折其髀，人皆弔之。其父曰："此何遽不爲福乎？"居一年，胡人大入塞，丁壯者引弦而戰，近塞之人，死者十九。此獨以跛之故，父子相保。

《淮南子·人間訓》

87   Blessing or Bane

Near China's northern borders lived a man well versed in the practices of Taoism. His horse, for no reason at all, got into the territory of the northern tribes. Everyone commiserated with him.

"Perhaps this will soon turn out to be a blessing," said his father.

After a few months, his animal came back, leading a fine horse from the north. Everyone congratulated him.

"Perhaps this will soon turn out to be a cause of misfortune," said his father.

Since he was well-off and kept good horses his son became fond of riding and eventually broke his thigh bone falling from a horse. Everyone commiserated with him.

"Perhaps this will soon turn out to be a blessing," said his father.

One year later, the northern tribes started a big invasion of the border regions. All able-bodied young men took up arms and fought against the invaders, and as a result, around the border nine out of ten men died. This man's son did not join in the fighting because he was crippled and so both the boy and his father survived.

Huainanzi

八十八　田子方見老馬

　　田子方見老馬於道，喟然有志焉，以問其御曰：“此何馬也？”其御曰：“此故公家畜也。老罷而不爲用，出而鬻之。”田子方曰：“少而貪其力，老而棄其身，仁者弗爲也。”束帛以贖之。罷武聞之，知所歸心矣。

《淮南子·人間訓》

88 An Old Horse

Tian Zifang saw an old horse on a road. He heaved a sigh, deeply moved.

"What horse is this?" he asked his carriage driver.

"Master, this horse used to be kept by you," replied the driver. "Since it is old and weak, it is not much used, so it was taken out to be sold."

"To exploit its strength in its youth and then get rid of it in its old age is not the way a man with decency and honour should behave."

Therefore Tian Zifang used five rolls of silk to buy back the horse. When old veterans heard of this, they were full of admiration and respect for him.

Huainanzi

八十九　螳螂搏輪

　　齊莊公出獵，有一蟲舉足將搏其輪。問其
御曰：“此何蟲也。”對曰：“此所謂螳螂者
也。其爲蟲也，知進而不知卻，不量力而輕
敵。”莊公曰：“此爲人而必爲天下勇武矣。”
迴車而避之。勇武聞之，知所盡死矣。

　　　　　　　　　　　　　　　　《淮南子・人間訓》

89 The Indomitable Mantis

Duke Zhuang of the state of Qi was out hunting when an insect lifted its legs and was about to fight with the wheel of his carriage.

"What insect is this?" the duke asked his carriage driver.

"This is called a mantis," replied the driver. "This insect only knows how to advance and never retreats. It overestimates its own strength and underestimates its enemy."

"If this is a man," said the duke, "he would be one of the bravest in the world."

He turned his carriage to avoid the mantis. When men of courage heard of this they realized to whom they could be loyal unto death.

Huainanzi

九十　與少望奢

　　威王八年，楚大發兵加齊。齊王使淳于髡
之趙請救兵，齎金百斤，車馬十駟。淳于髡仰
天大笑，冠纓索絕。王曰：“先生少之乎？”
髡曰：“何敢！”王曰：“笑豈有說乎？”髡
曰：“今者臣從東方來，見道傍有禳田者，操
一豚蹄，酒一盂，祝曰：‘甌窶滿篝，汙邪滿
車，五穀蕃熟，穰穰滿家。’臣見其所持者狹
而所欲者奢，故笑之。”

　　於是齊威王乃益齎黃金千溢，白璧十雙，
車馬百駟。髡辭而行，至趙。趙王與之精兵十
萬，革車千乘。楚聞之，夜引兵而去。

《史記·滑稽列傳》

90 Exorbitant Demands

When King Wei ruled the state of Qi, armies from the state of Chu attacked Qi in the eighth year of his reign. The king wanted Chunyu Kun to go to the state of Zhao and ask for troops to come to the rescue. Chunyu Kun was to take with him as presents one hundred catties of gold and ten carriages each drawn by a team of four horses.

Chunyu Kun threw back his head and laughed so much that all the tassels of his hat broke.

"Sir," said the king, "do you think that the presents are too meagre?"

"Sire, how would I dare to harbour such thoughts?" replied Chunyu Kun.

"Then why do you laugh?" asked the king.

"Today on my way here from the east, I saw a man praying to the heavens for a good harvest by the side of the road. He held up a leg of pork and a jar of wine to offer to the gods, praying as he did so, 'May the narrow fields high up the slopes produce enough to fill many baskets; may the fields in the low flat lands produce enough to fill many carts; may all the food crops grow in abundance; may my house be chockfull of grain.' His offering was so pitiful and his demands so exorbitant that I could not help laughing."

Therefore the king added one thousand and five hundred catties of gold, ten pairs of white jade ornaments and one hundred four-horse carriages. Chunyu Kun took leave of the king and went to Zhao. The king of Zhao let him have a hundred thousand well-trained soldiers and one thousand chariots. When the state of Chu heard of this, their troops were withdrawn in the dead of night.   *Shiji* (Records of the Historian)

九十一　雞有五德

　　田饒事魯哀公而不見察。田饒謂魯哀公曰：「臣將去君而鴻鵠舉矣。」哀公曰：「何謂也？」田饒曰：「君獨不見夫雞乎？頭戴冠者，文也；足搏距者，武也；敵在前敢鬬者，勇也；見食相呼，仁也；守夜不失時，信也。雞雖有此五者，君猶日瀹而食之，何則？以其所從來近也。夫鴻鵠一舉千里，止君園池，食君魚鼈，啄君菽粟，無此五者，君猶貴之，以其所從來遠也。臣請鴻鵠舉矣。」

　　哀公曰：「止！吾書子之言也。」田饒曰：「臣聞食其食者不毀其器，蔭其樹者不折其枝。有士不用，何書其言為！」遂去之燕。

91 The Cock and the Wild Swan

Tian Rao served Duke Ai of the state of Lu but the duke did not appreciate his abilities.

"My lord," said Tian to the duke, "I am going to leave you as a wild swan takes off to the skies."

"What do you mean?" asked the duke.

"My lord, have you not seen the cock?" said Tian. "On its head sits a red comb — this is elegance; on its feet are sharp spurs — this is might; faced with an adversary it is always ready to put up a fight — this is courage; at the sight of something to eat, it calls its companions to share the food — this is benevolence; as a sentry watching through the night, it never fails to announce the hour — this is faithfulness. Though the cock has these five virtues, you, my lord, still give orders that it be cooked and served as food. Why is that so? It is because the cock is nearby, at hand. As for the wild swan, with a flap of its wings it covers hundreds of *li*. Resting in your garden and your pond, it devours your fish and turtles, and pecks at your grain and beans. Even though it lacks these five virtues it is still cherished by you. This is because it comes from far far away. Please give me leave to go far away like the wild swan."

"Stay," urged the duke. "I will write down your words."

"I have heard," said Tian, "that one who accepts food from another does not destroy the vessels; and one who enjoys the shade of a tree does not break its branches. If a capable man is not given the chance of using his abilities, what is the use of writing down his words?"

Tian left Lu and went to the state of Yan where

燕立以爲相。三年，燕之政大平，國無盜賊。哀公聞之，慨然太息，爲之避寢三月，抽損上服曰：「不愼其前而悔其後，何可復得！」

《新序・雜事五》

he was appointed prime minister. After three years, Yan enjoyed peace and prosperity and not a thief was found in the whole state. This came to the ears of Duke Ai who sighed with deep regret. Because of this he lived in solitude for three months and did away with many of his luxuries.

"Because of my own negligence in the past," he said, "I am now filled with regret. Nevermore can I hope to regain what I have lost."

Xinxu

九十二　葉公好龍

　　葉公子高好龍，鈎以寫龍，鑿以寫龍，屋
室雕文以寫龍。於是夫龍聞而下之，窺頭於
牖，施尾於堂。葉公見之，棄而還走，失其魂
魄，五色無主。是葉公非好龍也，好夫似龍而
非龍者也。

《新序・雜事五》

92   The Real Thing

Lord Ye, styled Zigao, was fond of dragons. He had dress ornaments and wine cups with the pattern of dragons, and all the carvings in the rooms of his house were in the shape of dragons. As a result, the real dragon heard about this and came down to his house. It stuck its head through a window to take a peep while trailing its tail in the hall. Lord Ye saw it and turned to flee with a terrified look on his face, frightened out of his wits.

This man was not really fond of dragons. He was only fond of what looked like a dragon but was not a dragon in reality.

Xinxu

九十三 中天臺

　　魏王將起中天臺，令曰：「敢諫者死。」

　　許綰負藁[1] 操鍤入，曰：「聞大王將起中天臺，臣願加一力。」王曰：「子何力有加？」綰曰：「雖無力，能商臺。」王曰：「若何！」曰：「臣聞天與地相去萬五千里，今王因而半之，當起七千五百里之臺。高既如是，其趾須方八千里，盡王之地，不足以為臺趾。古者堯舜建諸侯，地方五千里，王必起此臺，先以兵伐諸侯，盡有其地；猶不足，又伐四夷，得方八千里，乃足以為臺趾。林木之積、人徒之

⑴據〔唐〕馬總撰《意林》補。

93　Halfway Up the Skies

When the king of Wei decided to build a tower that would reach halfway up the skies, he gave an order: "Anyone who tries to dissuade me will be put to death."

Xu Wan, a minister of Wei, came to the presence of the king, carrying a dirt basket on his back and holding a spade in his hand.

"Sire, I heard that you are about to build a tower that would reach halfway up the skies," said Xu, "your humble servant would like to offer a helping hand."

"What strength have you got to offer?" asked the king.

"I may be lacking in strength," replied Xu, "but I can help in the planning of this construction."

"Well?" inquired the king.

"Sire, I have heard the distance between heaven and earth is fifteen thousand *li*. Now since you want to build a tower that reaches midway up the skies, the tower should be seven thousand five hundred *li* tall. With a structure that tall, the foundations must have a circumference of eight thousand *li*. Not all your lands together, sire, is enough for the foundations. In ancient times, the monarchs Yao and Shun established dukedoms which had a circumference of five thousand *li*. If you are determined to build this tower, you must first attack the dukes and take over all their lands. That is still not enough. You must also subdue the various barbarous tribes living in the far away regions to our north, south, east and west. When you have got an area with a boundary of eight thousand *li,* it will be adequate for the foundations. As for building materials, workers and stores of food, all these must be calculated by

眾、倉廩之儲，數以萬億；度八千里之外，當
定農畝之地足以奉給王之臺者。臺具以備，乃
可以作。”

魏王默然無以應，乃罷起臺。

《新序·刺奢》

hundreds of millions. Outside the area bound by eight thousand *li*, a large number of fields must be designated for producing food to feed the workers constructing the tower. When all the conditions for building the tower are met, the work can begin."

The king was silent, unable to think of a reply. He gave up the idea of building the tower.

Xinxu

九十四　秦西巴釋麑

　　孟孫獵，得麑，使秦西巴持歸。其母隨而鳴。秦西巴不忍，縱而與之。孟孫怒而逐秦西巴。居一年，召以爲太子傅。左右曰：“夫秦西巴有罪於君，今以爲太子傅，何也？”孟孫曰：“夫以一麑而不忍，又將能忍吾子乎？”

　　　　　　　　　　　　　　　　《說苑・貴德》

94   Compassion for a Fawn

When Meng Sun was out hunting he caught a fawn which he entrusted to Qin Xiba to take home. The mother deer followed Qin, crying piteously. Qin Xiba was touched so he let the fawn go with its mother. As a result, Meng Sun was so incensed that he banished Qin.

After one year, Meng summoned Qin and appointed him to the post of the crown prince's tutor.

"Qin offended you in the past," pointed out his close attendants. "Why are you appointing him to be the crown prince's tutor?"

"If Qin had compassion even for a little fawn," replied Meng, "will he not be good to my son?"

Shuowan

九十五　螳螂捕蟬

　　　　吳王欲伐荆，告其左右曰：“敢有諫者死。”舍人有少孺子者，欲諫不敢，則懷丸操彈遊於後園，露沾其衣。如是者三旦。吳王曰：“子來，何苦沾衣如此？”對曰：“園中有樹，其上有蟬。蟬高居悲鳴飲露，不知螳螂在其後也。螳螂委身曲附欲取蟬，而不知黃雀在其傍也。黃雀延頸欲啄螳螂，而不知彈丸在其下也。此三者皆務欲得其前利而不顧其後之有患也。”吳王曰：“善哉。”乃罷其兵。

《說苑・正諫》

95 The Mantis and the Cicada

The king of the state of Wu wanted to attack the state of Chu.

"Anyone who attempts to dissuade me," the king warned his ministers, "will be put to death."

Among those who served the king was a young man who wanted to dissuade the king but dared not. He took some pellets and went into the rear garden holding his catapult. He stayed there until his clothes were damp with dew. This went on for three successive mornings.

"Come here young man," said the king, "is it worth getting your clothes so damp?"

"There is a tree in the garden," replied the young man, "and on it was a cicada. High up in the tree, the cicada chirped shrilly and drank the dew, unaware that behind it lurked a mantis. The mantis crouched low in its hiding place, bent on getting the cicada, unaware that right next to it was an oriole. The oriole strained its neck hoping to peck the mantis, unaware that there was a catapult below. All three of them were only concerned with getting the advantage before them and were heedless of the disaster that came in from behind."

"Well said," pronounced the king. He gave up the idea of attacking Chu.

Shuowan

九十六　景公好弋

景公好弋，使燭雛主鳥而亡之。景公怒而欲殺之。晏子曰：“燭雛有罪，請數之，以其罪乃殺之。”景公曰：“可。”於是乃召燭雛，數之景公前，曰：“汝為吾君主鳥而亡之，是一罪也；使吾君以鳥之故殺人，是二罪也；使諸侯聞之，以吾君重鳥而輕士，是三罪也。”數燭雛罪已畢，請殺之。景公曰：“止。”勿殺而謝之。

《說苑·正諫》

96   A Broad Hint

Duke Jing loved to catch birds. He ordered Zhu Chu to be in charge of bird catching but Zhu let the captured birds fly away. Duke Jing was incensed and wanted to put Zhu to death.

"Zhu Chu is guilty," said Yanzi, "please let me enumerate the crimes he committed and then sentence him to death for his offenses."

"You may do so," said the duke.

Accordingly Zhu Chu was brought to the presence of the duke and Yanzi enumerated his crimes, "You are supposed to help our lord catch birds but you let them escape. This is your first offence. You caused our lord to put a man to death because the birds got away. This is your second offence. When the princes of the other states hear about this, they will think that our lord value birds more than men. This is your third offence."

After enumerating Zhu's crimes, Yanzi asked that Zhu be put to death.

"He should not be put to death," said Duke Jing. And so the duke not only did not kill Zhu but also extended his apologies to him.

Shuowan

九十七　白龍下清冷之淵

　　　　白龍下清冷之淵，化爲魚。漁者豫且射中
其目。白龍上訴天帝。

　　　　天帝曰：“當是之時，若安置而形？”白
龍對曰：“我下清冷之淵，化爲魚。”天帝曰：
“魚，固人之所射也。若是，豫且何罪？”

《說苑·正諫》

97   A Shrewd Judge

The white dragon (whose duty, according to legend, was to bear the king of the gods on its back) descended to the Qingling abyss and turned into a fish. A fisherman Yu Qie shot at it and hit its eye. The white dragon returned to the heavens and complained to the king of the gods.

"At that time what shape were you in?" asked the king.

"I descended to the Qingling abyss," replied the dragon, "and turned into a fish."

"A fish is the proper prey of a man," said the king. "In that case, what crime has Yu Qie committed?"

Shuowan

九十八　梟將東徙

梟逢鳩。鳩曰：“子將安之？”梟曰：“我
將東徙。”鳩曰：“何故？”梟曰：“鄉人皆惡
我鳴，以故東徙。”鳩曰：“子能更鳴可矣；
不能更鳴，東徙猶惡子之聲。”

《說苑‧談叢》

98   The Owl Intends to Move

An owl met a pigeon.

"Where are you off to?" asked the pigeon.

"I am moving to the east," replied the owl.

"Why are you moving?" asked the pigeon.

"The people here detest the sound of my hoots. That's why I am moving to the east."

"It would be a good thing if you could change the sound of your voice," said the pigeon. "If you couldn't, then when you have moved to the east, the people there will still detest your hooting."

Shuowan

九十九　周人不遇

　　昔周人有仕數不遇，年老白首，泣涕於塗者。人或問之：“何爲泣乎？”對曰：“吾仕數不遇，自傷年老失時，是以泣也。”人曰：“仕奈何不一遇也？”對曰：“吾年少之時學爲文，文德成就，始欲仕宦，人君好用老。用老主亡，後主又用武，吾更爲武，武節始就，武主又亡。少主始立，好用少年，吾年又老；是以未嘗一遇。”

　　仕宦有時，不可求也。

《論衡・逢遇篇》

218

99 The Man Who Never Got a Break

Long ago in the Zhou region (around present day Loyang city) was a man who, after repeated attempts, failed to start a career in the government. In his old age, covered with white hair, he wept by the side of the road.

"Why are you weeping?" he was asked.

"I have tried many times to obtain an official post," he answered, "but it was all in vain. Now I am old and can have no more opportunities. That is why I am weeping."

"How come you never had a chance of getting a good official post?"

"In my youth," replied the old man, "I studied to be a man of letters. When I became well-versed in literature and the arts and was ready to embark on a career in the civil service, the king preferred to employ older men. After the death of this king, his successor valued martial arts. Accordingly I turned from the pursuit of literature to applying myself to martial arts. When I became fairly accomplished in this field, the king died. The young king who came to the throne liked to have young men in his service. But by that time, I was already an old man. That is why I never had a chance of making good."

A career in government service depends on the right opportunities. It is not something that is within everyone's grasp, however hard one tries.

Lunheng

一〇〇 曲突徙薪

　　客有過主人者，見其竈直突，傍有積薪，客謂主人，"更爲曲突，遠徙其薪，不者且有火患。"主人嘿然不應。俄而家果失火，鄰里共救之，幸而得息。於是殺牛置酒，謝其鄰人，灼爛者在於上行，餘各以功次坐，而不錄言曲突者。人謂主人曰："鄉使聽客之言，不費牛酒，終亡火患。今論功而請賓，曲突徙薪亡恩澤，燋頭爛額爲上客耶？"主人乃寤而請之。

《漢書·霍光傳》

100   Prevention and Cure

A man visited his friend's house and saw that his kitchen range had a very straight chimney by the side of which was stacked a lot of firewood.

The visitor said to his host, "You ought to make the chimney crooked and move the firewood far away from it, or else you will easily have a fire on your hands."

His host made no answer. Not long afterwards a fire really broke out. With the help of his neighbours he was fortunate enough to put out the fire. Therefore, he killed his calf and prepared a feast to express his gratitude to his neighbours. Those who were scorched by the flames were given the places of honour and the rest were seated according to the amount of service they rendered. But the man who suggested changing the chimney and removing the firewood was not invited.

One of the guests said to the host, "If you had listened to your friend, you would not have had a fire and there would be no need to kill the calf and prepare a feast. Now when you invite your guests because of what they did for you, are you going to pass over the one who advised you to take precautions and merely honour those who were hurt by the flames?"

The host realized his oversight and invited his friend.

Hanshu (History of the Former
Han Dynasty)

參考書目
Bibliography

孟子正義　諸子集成　中華書局　1978年8月一版

Mengzi zhengyi or The Works of Mencius (with commentaries), from *Zhuzijicheng* (Collected Writings of Pre-Qin Philosophers), Chung Hwa Book Company 1978

莊子集解　諸子集成　中華書局　1978年8月一版

Zhuangzi jijie or The Works of Zhuangzi (with commentaries), from *Zhuzijicheng* (Collected Writings of Pre-Qin Philosophers), Chung Hwa Book Company 1978

列子注　諸子集成　中華書局　1978年8月一版

Liezi zhu or The Works of Liezi (with annotations), from *Zhuzijicheng* (Collected Writings of Pre-Qin Philosophers), Chung Hwa Book Company 1978

尹文子　諸子集成　中華書局　1978年8月一版

Yinwenzi or The Works of Yinwenzi, from *Zhuzijicheng* (Collected Writings of Pre-Qin Philosophers), Chung Hwa Book Company 1978

荀子集解　諸子集成　中華書局　1978年8月一版

Xunzi jijie or The Works of Xunzi (with commentaries), from *Zhuzijicheng* (Collected Writings of Pre-Qin Philosophers), Chung Hwa Book Company 1978

韓非子集解　王先愼注　藝文印書館　1969年10月再版

Wang Xianshen (annot.), *Hanfeizi jijie* or The Works of Hanfeizi (with commentaries), published by Yiwen Yinshuguan 1969

呂氏春秋　諸子集成　中華書局　1978年8月一版

Lüshi chunqiu or Historical Writings Compiled by Lü Buwei, from *Zhuzijicheng* (Collected Writings of Pre-Qin Philosophers), Chung Hwa Book Company 1978

晏子春秋　諸子集成　中華書局　1978年8月一版

Yanzi chunqiu or Historical Anecdotes of Yanzi, from *Zhuzi-jicheng* (Collected Writings of Pre-Qin Philosophers), Chung Hwa Book Company 1978

宓子　玉函山房輯佚書目

Fuzi or The Works of Fuzi, from *Yuhanshanfang jiyishumu* (Edited Lost Titles of Yuhanshanfang)

景子　玉函山房輯佚書目

Jingzi or The Works of Jingzi, from *Yuhanshanfang jiyishumu* (Edited Lost Titles of Yuhanshanfang)

戰國策　高誘注　藝文印書館　1974年3月三版

Gao You (annot.), *Zhanguoce* or Strategies of the Warring States, published by Yiwen Yinshuguan 1974

韓詩外傳　龍溪精舍叢書

Hanshi waizhuan or Han Ying's Illustrations of the Didactic Application of the Book of Songs, from *Longxi jingshe congshu* (Longxi Jingshe Series)

禮記　十三經注疏　中文出版社　1971年9月初版

Liji or The Book of Rites, from *Shisanjing zhushu* (The Thirteen Classics with Annotations), Zhongwen Publishing Company 1971

淮南子　諸子集成　中華書局　1978年8月一版

Huainanzi or The Works of Huainanzi, from *Zhuzijicheng* (Collected Writings or Pre-Qin Philosophers), Chung Hwa Book Company 1978

史記　司馬遷撰　中華書局　1959年9月第一版

Sima Qian, *Shiji* or Records of the Historian, Chung Hwa Book Company 1959

新序　劉向著　漢魏叢書　〔明〕陳榮刻本　新興書局

Liu Xiang, *Xinxu*, from *Han Wei congshu* (Han and Wei Series), Xinxing Book Company

説苑　劉向著　漢魏叢書　〔明〕陳榮刻本　新興書局

Liu Xiang, *Shuowan,* from *Han Wei congshu* (Han and Wei Series), Xinxing Book Company

論衡　王充　諸子集成　中華書局　1978年8月一版

Wang Chong, *Lunheng,* from *Zhuzijicheng* (Collected Writings of Pre-Qin Philosophers), Chung Hwa Book Company 1978

漢書　班固　中華書局　1970年版

Ban Gu, *Hanshu* or History of the Former Han Dynasty, Chung Hwa Book Company 1970